Moisey

KU-362-720

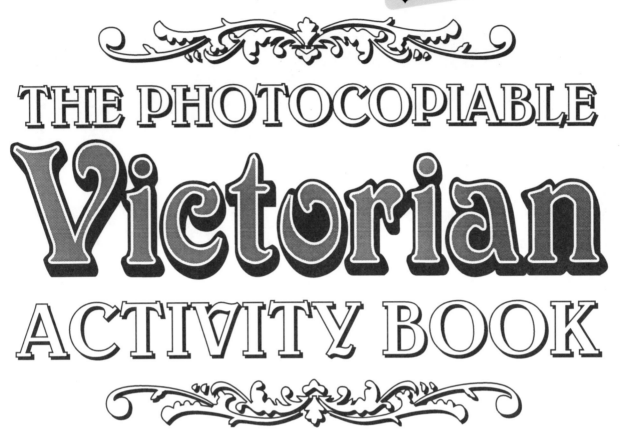

THE PHOTOCOPIABLE Victorian ACTIVITY BOOK

Written by Peter Bell and Paul Duckworth

Illustrated by John Hutchinson

Art Ideas by Diane Williams

A photocopiable Teacher Resource Book for Primary classes
studying the Victorian Era

James Alton Primary School
Morriston Street
Cambuslang
Glasgow
G72 7HZ

Published by

Topical Resources

Victorian Britain

by _____

Class _____

© Topical Resources. May be photocopied for classroom use only.

Introduction

Contents

A "Topic" is an approach to teaching in a Primary School which involves various apparently unrelated tasks being carried out under the umbrella of a common title or theme such as "Victorian Britain".

Topic work always:

> Includes class, group and individual work with some elements of choice.

> Involves practical activities.

> Uses themes selected which are thought appropriate to the interests and stage of development of children involved.

> Involves first hand experiences such as visits or visitors.

> Involves some sort of investigation.

> Involves using information gathering skills.

> Crosses some curriculum boundaries.

> It should also include, if possible an element of **"FUN"**.

The purpose of this book is to provide a bank of ideas and photocopiable activities, based on a Victorian Britain Study, which fulfil the above criteria. It is envisaged that a busy class teacher will use his/her professional judgment to select activities appropriate to their own individual situation.

Copyright © 1994
Peter Bell & Paul Duckworth
Illustrated by John Hutchinson
Art Ideas by Diane Williams
Printed in Great Britain for
"Topical Resources"
Publishers of Educational Materials,
P.O. Box 329, Broughton, Preston. PR3 5LT
Telephone 01772 863158
by T.Snape & Company Ltd.,
Boltons Court, Preston.

Typeset by "Topical Resources"
First Published September 1994.
ISBN 1 872977 19 7

Background Information for Class Lessons

Life in Victorian Britain

Queen Victoria was on the English throne longer than any other reigning monach. She was crowned in 1837 and died in 1901 - a reign of sixty four years. It was a time of many changes:

The railways, which were invented just before Victoria came to the throne, spread throughout the country enabling many people to travel much more easily than before. Goods, letters and parcels could be sent and the sea-side resort was invented!

The cities grew in size swollen by poor country folk flocking to the towns to look for work and a better way of life. They came to work in mills and other newly mechanised factories but the conditions were often hard and the pay poor. They lived in the many small terraced back to back houses which were often found in the slum areas whilst at the same time many new large mansion type houses were built to house the factory owners, their families and servants.

These years were also a time of social reform. Among the changes made were laws to stop children being allowed to work in mines or as chimney sweeps. In 1870 a new Education law was passed to say that all children between the ages of 5 and 13 must go to school.

Queen Victoria's reign was also a time of great discovery and invention. Until these times large parts of the African continent had remained unexplored by europeans but discoveries by David Livingstone and others changed this. Great inventions included the telephone, the motorcar and many others. A Great Exhibition was held to show the world what Britain could manufacture. Many everday things in use today such as the gas cooker, the sewing machine or the bicycle were first invented in "Victorian Times".

The Railways

Twelve years before Queen Victoria came to the throne George Stevenson opened the first public railway from Stockton to Darlington. The first train was pulled by Stevenson's own engine called the "Locomotion". It travelled at 12 miles per hour. Other railways were soon to follow. At the start of Victoria's reign there were already 200 miles of track, and at the end there were over 20,000.

Up until this time most ordinary people had travelled everywhere by foot, stage-coaches being reserved for those that could afford them. Transporting goods by horse and cart along roads made mainly of earth, or mud after heavy rain, was an extremely difficult and hazardous process. The invention of the railways changed all this. Steam engines running on metal rails could pull large loads of passengers and goods very easily. Also, the Government insisted that railways must carry third class passengers at a penny a mile. This meant that poor people were given the opportunity to travel in a way never dreamt of before. People in towns could travel to the seaside and back in a day. The seaside resort was born, Blackpool being one of the most famous. Workers from the Lancashire mill towns such as Blackburn or Accrington could travel to the coast for a treat. Large towns also benefited. The goods they manufactured in their factories could now be sold up and down the country easily, greatly increasing the opportunities to trade. The Queen herself made use of the railways using them to visit her newly built homes in Balmoral, Scotland, and Osborne House on the Isle of White. A new age of travel had begun.

Living in the Towns

Victoria's reign saw large growth in the towns up and down the country. Farm workers moved away from the country in large numbers looking for better paid work in the new factories that were springing up everywhere. Rows and rows of workers cottages were built but the were often very small and suffered from poor sanitation. The water supply was often filthy and diseases such as cholera spread easily from house to house. It wasn't until 1875 that a law was passed which forced the authorities to clean up the drains and sewers and make sure the drinking water was pure.

Other advances in health occurred when James Simpson introduced anaesthetics for operations and Joseph Lister introduced antiseptics to lesson the risk of infection in wounds. Florence Nightingale through her work in nursing also made people aware of the need for cleaner conditions for the sick.

Life in a Terraced Row

The poorer houses in the towns were usually small terraced houses with no gardens and an outside closet. (toilet) This may even have been shared. Water supplies also were shared with many families using the same pump or tap. In this way diseases were easily spread.

Inside the houses would not be large having one or two rooms downstairs with the same above. Families however were large, six or seven children being the norm, and so few were afforded the luxury of a bed of their own. The girls would share one and the boys another. Sometimes an additional "bedplace" could be found under the stairs.

The house would be heated by coal fires which also provided heat for cooking and hot water.

Large families required lots of cooking and washing all of which was hard work. Wash day would be typically on a Monday when large quantities of hot water were heated on the fire to fill a tub. The clothes were moved around in the hot water using a "dolly peg", rinsed and dried inside hung on a clothes rack. Flat irons, again heated on the coal fire, would be used to iron the clothes when dry. A metal hob could be swung over the fire to heat a kettle or a pan. The oven, also heated by the fire, was used to make bread.

Terraced houses did not have the luxury of a bathroom. A tin tub would be placed in front of the fire and filled with hot water. The girls would be sent to bed early and the boys would take turns to use the same water to bathe in. On another evening the boys would go to bed early and the girls would bathe.

Victorian homes had no electricity with light being provided by oil or gas lights. The growth of factories which mass produced goods meant that even humble homes could now afford some luxuries such as curtains and rugs. However, because most homes were rented, many lived in fear of getting behind with the rent and eventually being put out on the street.

The Wealthy Homes

Not all families were poor in Victorian Times. Some families lived in larger terraced houses with small gardens back and front and enjoyed such luxuries as their own water taps and gas lighting. These homes would have a "maid of all work" who slept in the attic and whose job it was to to do the housework. The more wealthy families built large mansion type houses in the most pleasant parts of the town. These houses would have attics and basements for the servants to live and

work in with a second set of stairs at the back of the house for the servants to use. The children that lived in these homes were well protected from the terrible poverty found in the streets nearby.

Wealthy children would not go to school. Instead a tutor or governess would be employed to teach them at home. As they got older the boys would be sent away to boarding school whilst the girls stayed at home to learn needlework, piano playing and how to run a home. The family would be attended to by a team of servants each with different jobs to do. Teenage country girls would take jobs as maids to "see the world", send a little money home to help feed large families and hopefully find a husband.

For the servants the working day started very early so they could clean the grates and make the coal fires for the family getting up. The days were long being filled with many manual tasks including polishing shoes, sweeping floors, scrubbing steps and polishing cutlery. If a member of the family wanted a bath the water had to be heated over a fire and carried upstairs in jugs until the bath was full.

Small children would spend most of their time in the nursery looked after by a nanny. They would have toys such as jigsaws, a toy theatre, clockwork models and a rocking horse to play with. Their meals would be served to them here and not until they were of tutoring age would they have meals with their parents.

Children at Work

Poverty and hunger, caused by having large families and poorly paid work for the men, meant that many women and children had to work to help the family survive.

Children could start work as young as six or seven years old. Women and children were used to move the heavy carts of coal in the coal mines, dirty heavy work which required a lot of bending down. Small boys would sit for hours on their own in cold, wet and draughty tunnels operating trap doors to provide ventilation for the mines. Children who worked in mills had to crawl around under noisy machinery collecting loose cotton. This work was extremely dangerous as one wrong move could result in a limb or your hair being caught in the moving machinery! Small boys were sent up chimneys to clean them out. To prepare them for this their master would rub salt water into their knees and elbows until they bled. Repeatedly doing this made the skin grow hard but was an extremely painful process. The days were long for working children often lasting twelve or fourteen hours a day. Many poor children could be seen on the streets of the big towns and cities sweeping crossings, shining shoes, begging or even stealing.

During Victoria's long reign many people tried to improve the lot of working children. Lord Shaftesbury was one of these. In 1833 a law was passed banning children under 9 working in mills. In 1940 a law was passed forbidding children to be used to clean chimneys, but these laws were hard to enforce and ignored by many people. In 1842 a law was passed to stop children under 10 working in mines. As more and more social reformers became aware of the plight of working children conditions improved, and it was eventually agreed that children under the age of thirteen must not work longer than eight hours a day.

School for All

Schools had existed for many years before Victorian Times but they were only for the wealthy. Public schools existed for those that could afford the high fees, merchants and other high earners would pay to send boys to the Grammar School. Other children were taught at home by tutors or governesses.

Some villages had Dame schools where an older lady would teach a number of small children in one room of her house. Some of the more enlightened Factory Owners provided schools for the children of their workers. Churches started Sunday Schools to teach children who worked through the week to read the Bible. Out of these grew the Church Day Schools but many children still received no schooling at all.

In 1870 a law was passed which said that all children between the ages of five and thirteen must go to school. School boards were set up to build schools in areas where there were none. Parents were expected to pay a penny or two a day but this did not go down well with those that needed the income from their children being out at work. Some children, called half-timers, worked half the day and attended school for the other half.

Victorian schools were different from today's schools. The children sat in rows or stood in groups to be taught. A teacher may be in charge of between 60 to 80 pupils with monitors (older children) paid to help. Classes of up to 100 pupils were not unheard of! The teacher would keep control from a raised up desk from where he or she could see the whole class. Discipline was very strict with children receiving a beating from the cane for even minor offences.

The children did not work in age groups but in Standards. Once a year the school inspector would come to test the children to see if they had reached the required "Standard" to move into the next class. If not, they would repeat the year again resulting in children of various ages being mixed together. Children were taught to read, write, do sums, mental arithmetic and scripture.

Discovery and Exploration

Before the Industrial revolution most goods were made by hand by people working from their own homes. The Steam engine changed all this. Victorian times saw great growth in factories with powered machines. The railways improved the ability to trade and many other new inventions came along. These years transformed a rural society to the largely industry based society that we live in today.

The pneumatic tyre was invented and the bicycle as we know it today evolved from the Hobbyhorse. Steam powered ships sailed the world no longer dependent upon the wind. The petrol engine and the first motor cars were invented. Other inventions included gramophones, moving pictures, sewing machines, typewriters and the fountain pen. The first underground railway was built under the streets of London.

Improved printing techniques in printing brought down the price of newspapers and more and more people were learning to read. The penny post meant that people could send letters reliably anywhere in the country.

The early days of electricity brought an exhibition of home lighting in 1882. The telephone was invented as was wireless telegraphy. A cable was laid under the Atlantic Ocean to send and receive messages from America.

The invention of the refrigerator brought cargoes of frozen meat from Australia and New Zealand. The large growth of the population over the century resulted in many workers looking for new lives in distant places. Many emigrated to America, Australia, New Zealand and Africa. David Livingston and others continued exploration in parts of the African continent.

The Great Exhibition

In 1851 Queen Victoria opened the first world trade exhibition in the "Crystal Palace" built on Hyde Park in London. It was called "The Great Exhibition of the Works of Industry of All Nations". The idea for the exhibition came from Prince

Albert the Queen's husband. He wanted to show the world the new ideas and inventions being built in Britain at this time and give the British people the opportunity to see what other countries had to offer.

The exhibition was housed in a giant building designed by Sir Joseph Paxton especially for the event. It was made of prefabricated cast iron sections and glass and looked like a giant conservatory. It was so tall that 30 metre elm trees grew inside it. It had over 8 miles of display tables. On display were all manner of new inventions and manufactured goods including false teeth and artificial legs from America. Other exhibits included furniture, clothing, model cottages, clocks, silver, ribbons, lace, porcelain, embroideries etc. from many parts of the world.

The exhibition was a great success. Over 19,000 different goods were displayed and over 6 million people came to visit. At first just the more wealthy people came but these were soon followed by lots of ordinary working people travelling by train or just on foot. Visitors also came from all over the world and considered the event such a success than soon other countries followed with their own exhibitions. The Eiffel Tower, at that time the tallest building in the world, was built in 1889 for the Paris Exhibition.

After the exhibition was over the structure was taken down and rebuilt at Sydenham Hill in South London. It remained on this site until it burnt down in 1936. The remains of the foundations can still be seen today. The profits from the exhibition were used to build the Victoria and Albert Museum and the Science and Natural History Museums found in South Kensington, London.

The Workhouse

In Victorian Times people who had no work received no money at all. If they were old, sick, orphaned or simply could not find any work you were sent to the Workhouse. These were grim buildings where the destitute lived and worked.

People feared being sent to the Workhouse. The Government at the time believed that people without work should not be fed or housed any better than the poorest wage earner; but some wages were very low indeed. Husbands, wives, parents and children were split up. They slept in dormitories and were made to do long tedious work such as breaking up stones to build new roads. The food was very poor and there was barely enough of it to stay alive.

Visitors to the workhouses urged the Government to improve conditions. Old married couples that had spent most of their lives together were to be given a room to share but this was often not the case and they were separated. Girls and boys were allowed to attend the local Board Schools but they stood out from the other children with their cropped hair and unkempt appearance.

Over the course of Victoria's reign conditions slowly improved. However, it wasn't until the 20th Century that the Workhouse was finally abolished and replaced by a Social Security System.

The British Empire

An Empire is made when one country rules over a number of others. The Assyrians ruled vast areas of land from the 6th to the 4th Centuries B.C. The Roman Empire lasted until the 5th Century A.D. Europeans discovered "new parts of the world" due to the journeys of people such as Columbus to Central America and Cook to Australia and New Zealand. This culminated in a race for Africa in the late 1800's. As each place was discovered the European countries made claims to these distant lands, increasing the size of their Empires.

The British Empire became the largest of these European Empires. It consisted of what is now known as Canada, parts of America, parts of Africa, India, Australia, New Zealand and a number of other smaller "colonies" as they were called. It was said that, "The sun never set on the British Empire". The Victorians saw little wrong in these actions. They believed that "Europe was the civilised world" and so it was only natural that they should rule and civilise the rest. These colonies were established either by peaceful settlement or by forcibly conquering areas that were already settled. Once discovered, the usual pattern was for traders, soldiers and priests (to convert the natives to Christianity) to travel to these distant lands and set up safe trading posts. Cheap local labour would be exploited and trade commenced in local raw materials such as gold, fur, diamonds, spices etc. and goods produced at home. The Empire became a source of national pride.

The British Empire no longer exists. Since World War II most former colonies have achieved independence either through war or voluntary agreement. The Commonwealth is the name given to the collection of countries that used to be parts of the British Empire and still choose to meet regularly to improve trade and relations between its members. Many people from the Commonwealth countries and their descendants now live in Britain.

Victoriana

ART IDEAS ON THE THEME OF VICTORIAN BRITAIN

Many objects and designs remain popular and are copied and reproduced in the world today.

Make the children aware of this influence of 'art and design' from the past such as Victorian tiled fireplaces, brass lamps, Victorian conservatories. We also collect and display items from this age in our homes eg flat irons, candle sticks, glass bottles etc..

Victorian objects for display might include;

lamps:	oil or parafin
kitchen tools:	jelly moulds, scales, weights, mincers
candlesticks	
bottles:	medicine or lemonade
tea caddies	
keys	

plus catalogues showing examples of 'modern' Victoriana we incorporate in our homes today

All such items can be used successfully for observational drawing.

Large items e.g. treadle sewing machines could be observed and recorded piece by piece - the children drawing several small views focusing each time through a viewfinder before attempting the whole machine.

Patterns popular with Victorians and used by them in decoration on wallpaper, fabric etc. could become the starting point for the childrens own patterns e.g. looking at the shapes and colours used on Victorian tiles. Tartan or Paisley patterns could be extended and developed into the childrens own designs using similar colours and shapes - 'in the style of'!

Similarly observational drawings of flowers and foliage lend themselves to being repeated to become a 'William Morris' design. Remind the children of the symmetry within such designs and also emphasise the choice of original colour i.e. from a William Morris print.

Old lace, crochet and tatting - popular crafts used to decorate both Victorian homes and fashions can similarly be the starting point for either border or repeating patterns or circular designs.

These could be created in either black felt pen or chalk or black paper or cut paper. This could later be extended to further collage work using black, white, silver and grey cut shapes like stained glass window designs.

Plants favoured by the Victorians e.g. Aspidestra, Maiden Hair Fern, Parlour Palms could be brought in and drawn from observation. Their leaf shapes could be developed into pattern work using silhouettes. Decisions as to how to create the pattern could be gained by looking at wall paper or wrapping paper layouts e.g. stripes/overlays etc..

Similarly the leaf shapes could be modelled out of plasticene and the design produced by printing using ready mix paint.

Look for clues as to costume, housing, pastimes, modes of travel and events in the paintings of such Victorian artists as Atkinson Grimshaw, Walter Sickert, James Tissot, Ford Maddox Brown, Millais, J M Turner or Walter Longley.

Christmas cards often depict the Victorian scene and are worth collecting.

The paintings of L S Lowry give a picture of the industrial environment that emerged. Art movements that evolved during Victoria's reign include 'The Pre-Raphaelites, The Newlyn School and The Impressionists

With the children make a list of artists who belonged to these movements plus any examples of the pictures they produced.

Look for 'Victorian' style in the built environment
e.g. doorways, windows, railings, lamp posts, chimney pots, weather vanes, monuments, viaducts etc..

First make a list of what to look for. Make drawings or take photographs of Victoriana around the locality - from these a street of Victorian style houses could be made using junk materials.

A Victorian style monument for a present day celebrity could similarly be designed and made from junk.

Cameo silhouettes produced by cutting black paper were popular with the Victorians.
Use the overhead projector for the children to trace out one anothers profile and turn them into cameo silhouettes.

This same silhouette approach could be used to interpret well known Victorian stories as large scale pictures e.g.
Scrooge - A Christmas Carol
Alice in Wonderland
The Snow Queen

Alternatively silhouettes of interesting imaginary old characters in Victorian Costume with poke bonnets and frills could be created.

Victorian room settings could be made in a series of shoe boxes.
e.g. one could be a kitchen complete with range, dresser, sink etc. made from junk materials.

A drawing of 'my family' in Victorian costume could be produced alongside 'my family' in modern dress. Each could be displayed in a decorative oval shaped frame like a Victorian photograph frame.

A frieze of the class in Victorian dress is another possibility with a Victorian school room as the background.

Look at Victorian advertisements for household products - design an advertisement for one of todays popular household products but do it in the 'Victorian' style.

The Victorians loved to clutter every available horizontal surface with ornaments either collected or made.
Discuss the ornaments we have in our homes (brought back from holiday etc.).
Are any of them similar to Victorian ornaments?
  e.g. decorated boxes, china houses,
        toby jugs?
Such ornaments could be made
  e.g. by covering boxes with shells or painting flower pots with brightly coloured birds, fruit or flowers or Egyptian figures - all designs favoured by the Victorians:

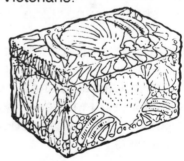

A dried flower dome can be made using a plastic lemonade bottle. Pull off the base, cut off and discard the neck end of the bottle. Glue a piece of oasis into the bottle base using P.V.A. glue. Arrange dried flowers and grasses in the oasis and then place the dome over the arrangement.

Collect and press flowers. When they are flattened and dried use them to create a picture or book mark as the Victorians did. Another approach would be to explore and develop paper skills - scoring, cutting etc. using stiff paper. These could be used to create different types of flower heads and these flowers could then be used to create a flower picture or (if 3-D) a Victorian posy.

Quilling was another popular Victorian pastime. Use brightly coloured paper cut into 1cm strips. Curl the strips around a knitting needle to form a coil. To make a scroll curl half a strip of paper in one direction and the other half in the opposite direction. Use the shapes to create a border for e.g. creative writing or to decorate the lid of a box by fastening them down with glue.

Canal boat art could be explored as part of a Victorian project. The traditional colours and designs investigated, copied and then used to decorate paper plates and cups. Sticky paper and paint being the most appropriate media.

Samplers embroidered with the alphabet or a proverb were produced in the Victorian home. The children could design their own on squared paper using felt tip pens and a limited number of colours
e.g. 3 only for maximum impact.

Victorian Music Halls offered popular entertainment. Design a poster to feature a variety of artists for a music hall bill.

Sea bathing was now being enjoyed. Look for pictures of Victorian bathing costumes and bathing machines. Design a Victorian style bathing costume but use the face, hands and feet cut out of a colour magazine to create a figure in Victorian bathing dress. Make a row of bathing machines from junk materials - to match the bathing costumes.

Make rubbings of Victorian coins, floor grates, lettering on bottles and tins. Cut these out and make a collage Victorian style as would have been found in a scrap book.

Victoriana offers plenty of scope to develop a wide range of Art & Craft activities as hopefully you will now
discover
explore
and
expand

GATHERING ORAL EVIDENCE

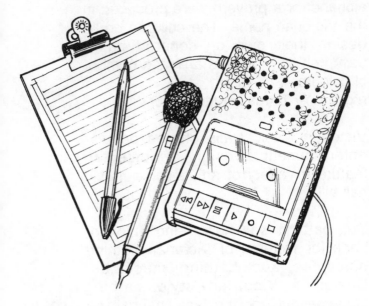

Interviewing elderly people provides a valuable collection of oral history which can be used over and over again to provide children with first-hand accounts of life in the past. Such primary evidence can prove hard to find and the benefits of recording people's memories can be reaped for years to come.

Interview with Mrs. Dutton (aged 99) by Moss Side CP School, Leyland

The oral history transcript that follows is a transcript of an interview carried out by Year 6 children of Moss Side County Primary School, Leyland as part of their study of Life in Victorian Britain. They arranged to interview Mrs. Dutton (born 23rd November 1892) at the local sheltered housing where she lived and the oral history extracts used in this book are taken from her discussions with the children.

How was the visit arranged?

The Class Teacher made all the arrangements with the Warden of the Sheltered Housing and arranged for the Warden to be there to relay the children's questions to Mrs. Dutton. It was arranged to interview Mrs. Dutton in the community centre of the sheltered housing and set up the karaoke machine so that Mrs. Dutton's responses would be amplified, which would be better for the children to hear and easier to tape! It was agreed that the teacher would take a sound recording of the interview.

How was the interview arranged?

For a few days before the visit the class teacher asked the children to submit questions to him that they would like to ask Mrs. Dutton. (Open questions are better than questions like 'Did you like school?'). He then sifted through these and grouped them so that questions on a similar theme would be asked together. The interview itself could then run like an edition of 'Question Time' with the teacher introducing the different questioners. On the morning of the interview the children were given their questions back with a number on them so that they knew in which order they were to be asked. They were encouraged to practise their questions so that they asked them with confidence and Mrs. Dutton could understand them clearly. At the end of the set questions there was a period of 'open' questioning and because of the careful preparation that had gone into the interview this was clearer and more useful than is sometimes the case when children are asked if they have any more questions!

How can this evidence be used?

The children were encouraged to listen to the tape on their return to school and chose one fact about Mrs. Dutton's childhood that they found interesting, and record this on a hexagon shaped piece of paper, giving it a victorian-style border. These were then displayed as a patchwork quilt of Mrs. Dutton's memories.

Oral Evidence can also be used when working on specific subjects such as 'Washing Day' or 'School' in Victorian Britain, with the teacher selecting bits of the transcript to use as evidence for the children to work with.

Points to Remember

* Plan the interview carefully.

* Tape the interview for future reference and, if possible, write a transcript of it.

*Allow the children to ask their own questions and experience what a valuable source of information our elderly people can be. Left to it children and old people can talk for hours!

TRANSCRIPT

of interview with Mrs. Dutton (born 23rd November 1892)
by Year 6 of Moss Side County Primary School, Leyland
8th October 1992

What was your house like when you were young?

Eh? The house? Well we'd four bedrooms and we'd a sitting room and a kitchen and a back kitchen. It was four an' six a week. You didn't pay rent like you do today. That was for a house.

What was it like inside?

Well... They weren't furnished like they are today: People hadn't the money, but we did our best, and they were always clean, but we didn't worry much.

What were your floors like? The kitchen and that. Your floors?

What was what?

The floors...

Well they were flag floors but we had them covered with home-made rugs so they were warm.

What was your bedrooms like?

Well it were just our beds and a dressing table in but we'd a nice little window, we could sit in it and we could see for miles 'cause we were right in the country. We weren't in the town. I were brought up in a village so you don't need to expect any town news.

What village were you brought up in?

Carnforth.

That's Cumbria.

I don't think I ever went to Lancaster 'til I was about 12 years old. We just stopped in the village, just went out to Gala days at other villages. There wasn't a lot of pleasure same as there is today and work was hard. They all worked long days, and six days a week.

Did you have any pets?

No. We only had... we had a cat, that was all. We didn't bother with animals. There was plenty in the country around us.

Did you have kind parents and what were they called?

Kind parents? Yes they were very kind and very good to us.

What were their names?

Do you mean their first names? Margaret and William.

Did you have any brothers and sisters?

Any what?

Brothers and sisters?

Yes, I'd quite a lot. They'd big families in those days, they weren't little ones.

How many?

Fifteen.

Fifteen?

Fifteen, and fourteen of us grew up.

Did you?

Most of them going on for seventy when they died.

Are you the oldest?

No. I were the middle one.

Oh you are the middle one. What did your father do for work?

He worked in the iron works. He drove a machine for breaking iron up. I don't know what it was called. He casted iron. There was an iron works. There isn't now, but there was an iron works and iron was casted out of the furnaces, and then it was in long pieces, picked up and carried by a crane to this machine and broken up into wagons. There wasn't much work... only iron works and the railway and then the farms around.

Were you very rich or were you very poor?

No. We were just ordinary. We didn't have spending money. We were lucky if we got a halfpenny on Saturdays. I wonder what they'd think about it now.

That wasn't very much was it?

No.

Did you have any running water in the house?

Any what?

Running water.

Yes. We'd running water but only cold. There was no hot water in houses in them days, no baths or anything like that. We'd cold water and it was warmed in a boiler beside the fire. See... and all the water for washing had to be boiled... had to be heated. Some houses had no water. They went down to a pump and just got the water with a pump so they'd no water. They had all the water to carry into the houses.

What was it like when you were at school? Is it better today?

They were happy days at school. We didn't... we had to walk it. Many a time some came nearly an hours walk to school. I'd about a twenty minute walk when I was three year old. No taxis. No motors for carrying... there wasn't a motor running then. You see they were only just starting. You could walk... you could skip to school down the main road. You didn't need to keep on the footpath.

No traffic... was there?

No traffic. There was horses. People that could afford it had a horse and trap. But...it was walking wherever you went.

Did you have a lady teacher or a man teacher?

We'd a man Head Teacher... but most of the others were ladies.

Was she a nice teacher yours?

I had a nice teacher but they all had a cane and you jolly soon got it. If you got a sum wrong you got caned for it. It hurt across your hand when you got it... They don't know they're born today.

What was your school called?

British... British School... That's what the name of it was... The British School.

At Carnforth?

Yes... Over the top from the main road. Well last time I went through it was still standing... There's a new one built further up the road, near where I lived. It was a field. There's a big school and houses there now. Things have altered a lot since then.

How many children were there in your class?

Oh... many times five or six on a desk... sometimes about fifty in a class. Some teachers had to manage two classes... They might have just quite a young girl helping, that was learning that was all. Drill was just what we could do in the playground. There was no proper places for us. There was no swimming or anything like that. There was really no pleasure with it... only they used to take us out for walks... just for... looking round the country you see and then we had to write essays on it when we came back.

What was your classroom like at school?

Well it was just an ordinary room with pipes round. It had no stove in. One room had a stove in... it fed all the school. There was a stove in the cloakrooms where we left our clothes, so they were dry when we came back out at dinner time, if they were wet in a morning. They were happy days. I don't care what anybody said. They were happier days than they get today.

Did you ever learn the Victorian Handwriting?

Yes, we had to do it good or we catched it. There was no mistakes in sums or you got caned. You made a mistake, he'd cane.

So you had to be clever?

Aye. I once took a sum to be marked and it had wrong on the answer she had, and I got caned twice for it. And then she didn't apologise she just said the answer was wrong on her sheet.

She was wrong and you were right. Was your teacher very strict?

Very strict. You daren't be late. You'd be skipping in or have to run. You daren't be late for school or you got caned. And you got caned if you got a sum wrong. The cane... the cane was always there. They knew about it... everybody knew about it... Still. We were quite happy. You know me... we didn't... children weren't miserable like a lot of them are today.

How much did you have to pay to go to school?

Tuppence a week, and we'd to buy our own exercise books. They were about a penny. That stopped while I were going to school. They stopped that... and they stopped the school money, the money for books. So we got a bit cheaper but it used to cost us tuppence every week going to school.

That was a lot of money wasn't it, tuppence?

It was a lot of money in them days. Yes. It was a lot was tuppence.

Were you happy as a child?

I was very happy. Yes. We were a very happy family. Yes. There's only two of us left now.

How old is your brother?

88

What was your childhood like in Victorian Times?

It was all right. I say... we never saw the Queen. You didn't see her like you do today... but she used to travel, when she was going up to Scotland, in a train, trimmed up like a City Roost. She lived in it while she was going travelling. They didn't travel in one day, not now like they do. I remember first seeing a motor car.

Tell them about that.

I say... I saw one when I was about five year old. We were marched out of school to line the main road, so that we could see. There was about ten passed us going through. I think they were going to Scotland, but... we'd never seen a car before, they'd never been through the village. It'd be about... I'd be about 5 year old 'cause I always remember that, seeing my first car.

That would be 1897.

Well it would be. They were in France but they were building motor cars in the 1880s, but they didn't get to running in them the same and they were only allowed 10 mile an hour.

Did you go to work as a child?

When I was about thirteen. Between thirteen and fourteen. Some left early and went to work in different mines and things but we never did. We just left school when it was getting time.

How much did you get paid when you started work?

I went to work, sometimes seven days a week, for half a crown... half a crown and my food.

12.5p in today's money. How many hours a day?

I went at seven in the morning and I'd about twenty minutes walk to get there and I came home about six. I haven't taken any harm with it.

We can see! Were you ever a weaver?

No. I went into service. There was nothing... There was no weaving places round there. We'd have had to go out into a town. You see... but the weavers started at six o'clock and they worked seven days... six days a week or half a day on Saturday, but they'd to be there at six. If they were about five minutes late they were locked out. They'd to go home again.

So what did you do at work?

I was... I went into service.

Explain what that is...

Well you went into somebody else's house to clean for them... you see... but I was there five years. I enjoyed it... see... I came to Preston just after the war started and they advertised for tram conductoress and I went as a tram conductor. I was a tram conductor for four years but that was war work. Women went on munitions, they went on the railway stations and women had never worked like that before. They'd always stopped at home. So we had to... we took over in the first world war that is. I worked four years on the trams. They were open backs, they weren't covered in. You got wet through sometimes. Then you'd to walk home. I'd half an hour's walk to get home where I was lodging. They don't know they're born today.

Did you have any sweets and, if so, what were they like?

Oh yes. Mother bought us so many. You could get a pound for a few coppers. We had some every morning to go to school. We were pretty well looked after. We were well looked after as children, comes to some, some were brought up anyway.

What sort of sweets were they?

Boiled sweets. They were hard but... you don't see them now. But they were good and they weren't like a lot of rubbish they sell today.

What was it like for you to go shopping as a child? Did you ever go shopping for your mum as a little girl?

Yes. Many a time. She... we used to go with two golden sovereigns. These'll never have seen them... you see. But we used to go to pay for the week's shopping and get what else we wanted for the weekend. Butcher's carts came round to the door... grocer's carts to anyone. They all came round with horse and carts... oil for your lamps. There was no gas in the houses. No. No electric. You couldn't go and switch a light on as you were going about. But we were happy. We'd fields to go and play in, we didn't... we weren't afraid of going in the roads or anything... and the roads were safe to skip in. Boys had hoops... well girls had hoops and all... down the main road. But we... there was no fear of running into anything

Can you remember any new inventions during the early part of your life?

The telephone came in very early. I think it started before my time but very few people had it, only just doctors and such like, very few people had it. It wasn't on every house same as it is today. Can't remember anything else special.

What did you do when you got bored?

Well I don't think I was ever. We were happy children. We enjoyed it.

Did you ever go on holiday when you were young?

We never went away. We never went away... never went out of the village. People didn't have holidays every year and when I worked on the trams in the first world war if you had a week off for holidays you had to stand it. You didn't get your wages. You had to carry on without.

So there was no holiday pay?

People came through to Morecambe and those places for a week's holiday. They brought most of their food with them, and their return fare. Many a time they'd nothing else to go back with. They'd to work a week to get their wages.

What kinds of transport were there?

Shank's pony

I don't think they know what that means.

No! You had to walk. There were no charabancs. They were run... got to running. They were just horse-drawn. You couldn't go far in them.

They don't know what a charabanc is?

No I don't suppose they do. And they used to go on a canal boat. We'd a Sunday school trip and they used to... we used to get on a canal boat and go down to the next village and have a field day then come back by boat. That was a day out.

What kind of food did you eat as a child?

Food? I never tasted margarine until after the war. The second war... we never had it in the first... but... the first world war we ran very short of food. The second world war we were rationed... rationed from the start. So we had to manage... see... but if you managed with about a quarter of a pound of bacon a week... a quarter... a two ounces of butter and such like... that's about all you... you got half a pound of sugar a week and very little meat. Sometimes you got none it just depended if they had it in the first world war. But the second world war it was rationed out more... they were ready for it.

What did you have on your bread when you were a little girl?

Well we had plenty of jam. There was always home-made jam, and stocked really good things. I mean garden produce... we grew... we'd our own garden and my father had an allotment beside... he grew for us you see. You didn't bare much on the shops for things like that... you got them yourself. We got a newspaper every night for a halfpenny. We used to pay thruppence a week for the Lancashire Daily Post. Of course money was... they didn't get big wages you see...

How much did they get?

Some men had to work for about twenty shillings. When I went... When I went on the trams we worked 60 hours a week and we'd 25 shillings. That had to pay for your board and lodgings and any pleasure. You could go to the pictures for a penny if you wanted to sit up in the gods... If you wanted to pay a bit more... when I were young there was no pictures... they used to come about once a year in a sort of fair ground and bring a living picture with them. That was a rare, special treat.

Do you remember any crimes being committed?

Any crimes? What was his name? I forget their names... There was a doctor in Lancaster murdered his wife and his children's nurse. Do you remember that? There was a man called Crippin. I think it was in... he murdered his wife and took a girl with him and was going to America and they caught him on the ship... fetched him back again. But they were hung in those days. I don't remember anybody else. I don't think the world was as wicked as it is today... It certainly wasn't as crowded.

Did you know any rich people?

Well there was plenty about but we didn't bother going with them. You know... there was Lord Derby at Liverpool and there was some at Lancaster. Remember there were plenty of farmers about. Mostly it was country you see... there wasn't as many works as there is. There were no motor works or anything like that because there were no motors. There was two or three about... different places.

Were there any pop stars when you were young?

There was no pop. There's no pop stars. There was no living pictures. They just moved. Talking came in the 1920s. I remember I couldn't go... I had a young baby but my husband went to see the first picture that came to Preston.

What was it called?

I were just trying to think. He was a black man. I can't just think of his name. It's just on my tongue end but I can't think of it just now.

It wasn't Al Jonson was it?

Yes. That was the first talking you see.

What sort of clothes did you have as a little girl?

We always wore pretty long frocks, over our knees, with stockings up to our knees, and the stockings were home knit. My grandma used to knit for us... and she was blind but she could knit stockings with anybody. We'd to keep a frock for Sundays. That wasn't allowed on in the week. We had to go to Sunday School and we were always dressed up for Sunday School.

How much do you think things have changed from your Victorian Times to now?

Big changes. Yeah. There wasn't the roads there is today... and the roads were safer to walk about on. You could go out and you weren't afraid of coming back. You see... but... I wouldn't like to walk so far now on the roads.

Mrs. Dutton rode a bike until she was 96. Didn't you used to ride a bike?

Yes. I've ridden a bicycle. You used to pay thruppence to learn. Thruppence an hour to learn on bicycles. There was bicycles about, plenty, and there was trains. You could go for a penny a mile on a train.

Do you prefer life in Victorian Times or in Modern Times?

Well I don't think so, no. But they are not comparable with these really you know. You never saw the queen. She didn't show herself like this one does. Just go out and play in the fields. All the holidays out in the fields. We used to have big hay-making and such like just for fun, we didn't get paid for it.

When you were poorly how much did you have to pay to go to the doctors?

A doctor was half a crown for a visit. Five shillings for a visit and half a crown for a bottle of medicine. They were afraid of sending for the doctor because they couldn't pay. Insurance came in about 1912 I think. Lloyd-George brought it in. You see... you started paying sixpence a week, and when you were sick you got 7'6d for a woman and 10 shillings for a man. And pensions for old people came in a bit before and my grand-mother was due for it. She was over 70. They had to be over 70 then. She got 3 shillings a week. She had a bit of money. It was 5 shillings for anybody as had nothing and 3 shillings for anybody as had a bit more, and it was quite some time before there was pension for all the older people. It started then.

Tell them about when you had your slates at school.

I had a slate and a pencil... when we were little, and then we got to exercise books... and we had to pay for them... we had to buy our own slates, take them home and scrub them. Teacher would probably have a sponge on her table and just pat all your slates... you'd have a rag with you to wipe them off. I don't think they had them in the Infant room. They did without until they got into the big room. I remember learning to dance in the Infants. We had dancing in there, yes.

Did you have any close school friends when you were at school?

I had two. We were good friends all the time. But we didn't go out at night because there was very little light outside in the winter. We'd to go out in the dark so we didn't go out at night. Now you can see almost like daylight. Yes. Well there was no electric you see, only gas lamps what they and and a man came and turned them on at a certain time and came in a morning and turned them off.

Was he the knocker-upper?

I remember hearing the knocker-up coming round. He'd a thing with a bush on the end and come patting at the windows.

What time was that?

Well it just depends. Railway men were knocked up sometimes 3 o'clock in the morning and other times. It wasn't much later people were knocked up. They were up themselves.

What time did you start school?

What time? Nine o'clock.

What time did you finish?

Four. Finish at 12 'til half past one in summer. Just 1 o'clock in winter so we come home early, so we could get home before dark... 'cause it were dark.

How old were you when your parents died?

I wouldn't be so far off 60 when my mother died. I was with her when she died. She died in Lancaster. I was living here but I went to see her that night to stop the night. My father was... 1930 something my father died.

How old was he when he died?

Dad was 82. Mother was 90.

Did you ever go to Lancaster when there was a hanging?

No. I never visited the castle. I've been round it a few times. I used to visit the park and go right up on the top. There was an observatory place right at the top... We'd to make our own pleasures. You didn't get pleasures same as you do today.

Were you healthy as a child?

Yes. I never had anything much. Not until I was... I was working on the trams... then I got ill... I'd a real bad year of it then. But I haven't ailed much really.

What did you wear on your feet when you were a child?

Clogs. Clogs. Everybody wore clogs. Feet were a lot healthier than they were today. They were... they were a lot better for your feet.

Can you remember your teacher's name?

Yes. Mr. Barnard was the Headmaster and Miss. Robotham was Headmistress of the baby's school. There was a Racquel Stoppard and there was a Marion Stoppard. Two sisters. Lambert. They never went to college. They just trained and carried on. Some you liked and some you didn't.

How many children have you had?

Me? I've had three. They're all pensioners.

Tell them how old your children are?

How old?.. Well there's two over seventy and one sixty-four.

When you were skipping at school with clogs on did you ever fall over?

No. We didn't and we used to make school slides down the school yard, and slide down them in frosty weather... and we had some bad winters then. We used to make our own pleasures then.

There were no school dinners then were there?

No. If you couldn't get home, in the winter you'd to have dinner from 12 to 1, well if you hadn't time to go home you had to take sandwiches and take some tea and warm it.. get your break there. They didn't have school dinners. There was nothing like that. I've cooked in school dinners. I was in charge of a canteen when I finished work. I knew what it was. In one canteen there was about twenty of us working in it and we cooked for 1700. So that was a big place. But I worked in a smaller one and looked after it for 7 of us, all women. I was in charge of it.

Where do your children live?

One lives near Manchester, one in Preston and one in Leyland.

What was your best friend called?

Margaret. I didn't really make friends to last so long... only I had one friend I worked... when I was working on the trams and we were friends 'til she died at 74 and I'd another friend I met when I was about 21 and I was friendly until she died at 74. But we got separated different times.

What are your children's names?

Margaret, Arthur and Frank (Francis).

When did electricity come into your house?

Well we went into a house in 1928... 27 and there was just electric lighting. There was no plugs just electric lighting. I had the plugs put in later on, when we'd been in a bit.

What toys did you get for Christmas?

Handkerchiefs, gloves and such like. We didn't get a lot of toys. They weren't making them in them days... not like they do today... might get a new umbrella something like that. We always had a good christmas dinner. We always had a goose. We always had a good christmas dinner... a good plum pudding.

Photocopiable Worksheets & Activities

© Topical Resources. May be photocopied for classroom use only.

Map of the British Empire 1886

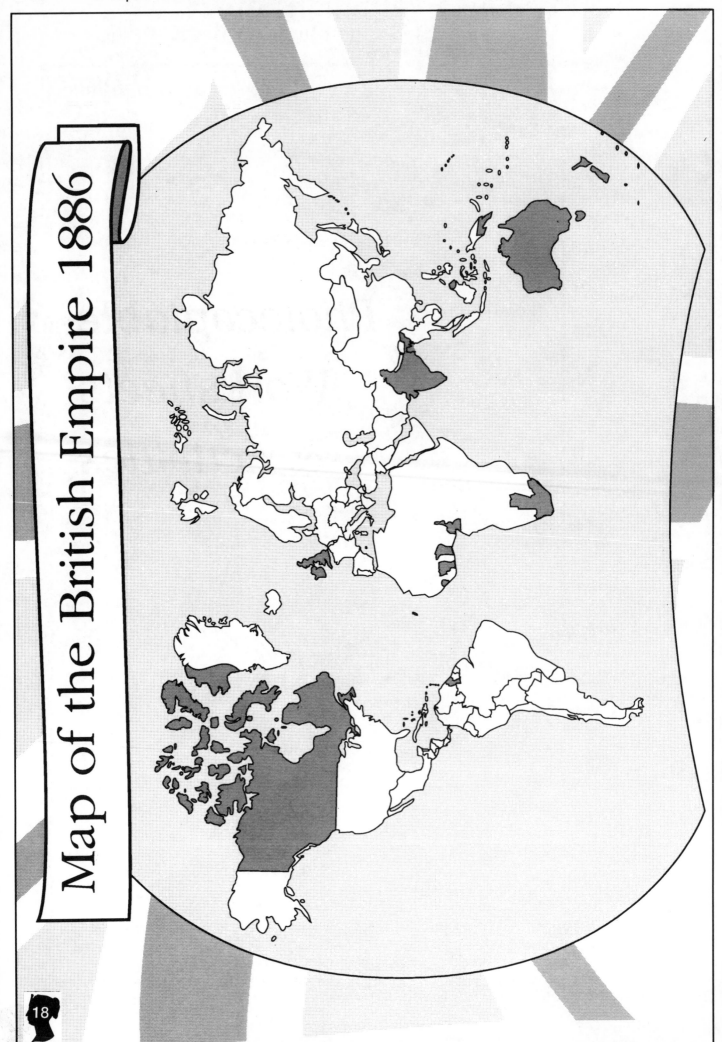

Self Evaluation Sheet
Victorian Britain Study Unit

Before you start this topic, write down everything you know about life in Victorian Britain:

_____

_____

_____

_____

_____

_____

_____

_____

At the end of the topic, write down, in note form, everything that you now know about life in Victorian Briatin.

_____

_____

_____

_____

_____

_____

_____

_____

_____

_____

_____

_____

_____

_____

_____

Compare what you now know with what you knew before you started this topic.

© Topical Resources. May be photocopied for classroom use only.

A SIMPLE TIME CHART: Where does this Topic fit in?

Earth Created	About 5000 million years ago	
Life in the Sea	About 500 million years ago	
Dinosaurs	About 150 million years ago	
Early Man	About 50 thousand years ago	
Ancient Egyptian Civilisation	About 4000 years ago	
Ancient Greek Civilisation	About 3000 years ago	
Roman Times	**B.C.** JESUS CHRIST IS BORN **A.D.** About 2000 years ago	
Anglo-Saxons invade Britain	About 1500 years ago	
Vikings invade Britain	About 1200 years ago	
Middle Ages	About 800 years ago	
World Wide Exploration & Encounters 1450 - 1550	About 500 years ago	
Tudors & Stuarts	About 400 years ago	
Victorian Britain	About 100 years ago	
Britain Since 1930	Over the last 60 years	

© Topical Resources. May be photocopied for classroom use only.

Victorian Britain Factsheet

Name...

I am researching:

_____

_____

_____

_____

Other areas I would like to know more about are:

_____

_____

_____

I have found out:

_____

_____

_____

_____

_____

_____

_____

_____

_____

_____

_____

_____

_____

_____

_____

You could use oral evidence (interviewing), written evidence in documents, objects, pictures, photographs, music, buildings or perhaps information on the computer

I used the following sources to help me:

_____

_____

_____

_____

_____

Put a star by the sources you found most useful.

© Topical Resources. May be photocopied for classroom use only.

Do you remember?

Does anyone in your family have any memories of what it was like to live in Victorian Britain? Even if you have no relatives who lived in that period, perhaps there is a story about your ancestors, what they did, or who they were, that you could find out about.

When you have found a family memory, write it in the shape below.

You can then designed a Victorian-style patterned or coloured border for around your hexagon.

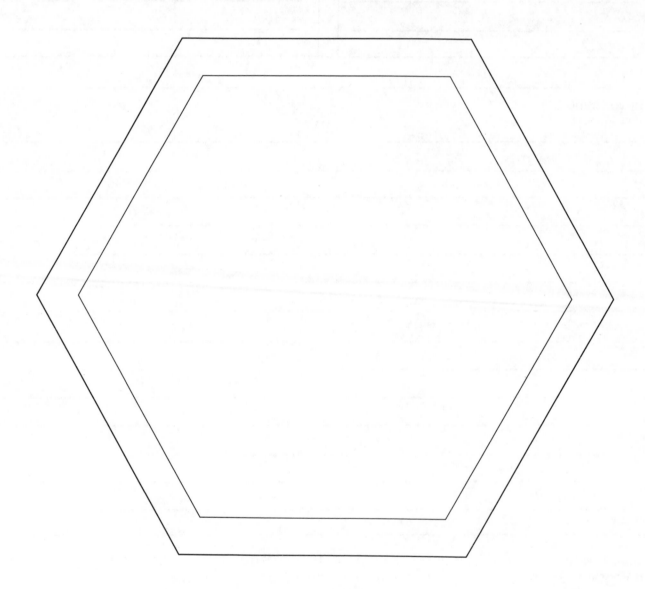

We can then cut out our hexagons and make a class patchwork quilt of Victorian memories.

PATCHWORK

Patchwork is the piecing together of shaped bits of fabric - often squares or hexagons. This craft, practised since early Egyptian times, was extremely popular in Mediaeval Europe, when it was used for dresses, wall and bed hangings and decoration. Patchwork quilts were designed in America by early settlers. The quilts became especially popular in the 18th and 19th Centuries and remain a popular art form in 20th Century America.

© Topical Resources. May be photocopied for classroom use only.

QUEEN VICTORIA'S FAMILY TREE

This family tree shows how the present Royal Family is related to Queen Victoria.

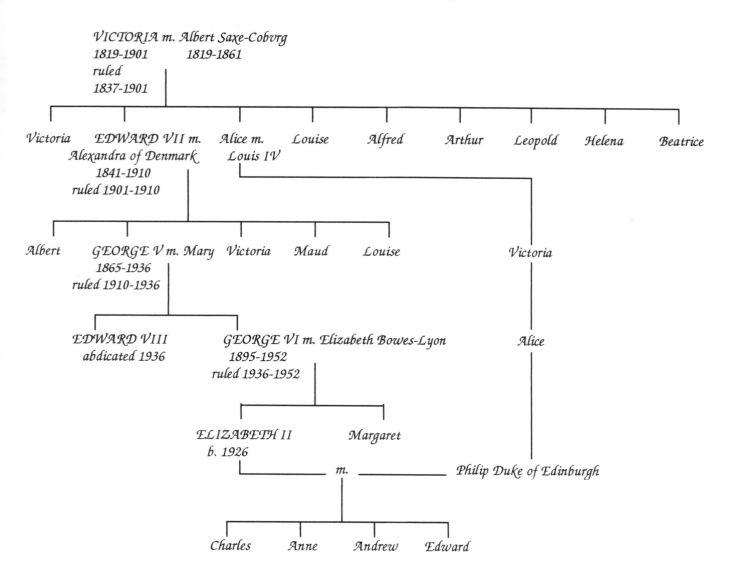

Write five questions that a friend could answer using the family tree

1 _____

2 _____

3 _____

4 _____

5 _____

Now swap sheets with a friend and try to answer each others questions.

Some members of the Royal Family are missing off this tree. Can you complete it?

© Topical Resources. May be photocopied for classroom use only.

I am Queen.....

"I was awoke at 6 o'clock by Mamma who told me that the Archbishop of Canterbury and Lord Conynham were here and wished to see me. Lord Conyngham then acquainted me that my poor Uncle, the King, was no more, and had expired at 12 minutes past 2 this morning and consequently that I am Queen."

If you awoke one morning and were told that you were the new King or Queen of England What would you think? say? do?
How would you change things?
(Remember: When Victoria became Queen she was only 18 years old.)

24 © Topical Resources. May be photocopied for classroom use only.

A Selection of Entries from the School Log Book of a Village National School July 1894 - July 1895.

July 12   Broke up at noon for mid-summer vacation.

Aug. 13   Reopened school this morning.

Aug. 17   Most of the farmer's children have been away from school this week.

Aug. 24   The average this week has increased from 77 last week to 86.

Aug. 28   Rev. G. Wilkes took the Scripture lesson this morning.

Sept.12   Holiday this afternoon for Conder Green Flower Show.

Sept. 17   Marked registers at 1.30 in order to close school a little earlier it being the Gas Light Flower Show. During the evening the children have been competing for prizes in Sewing, Drawing, and Writing.

Oct.19   Mr. J.Leeming , School Attendance Officer, called this afternoon.

Oct.22   Commenced fires to-day, the cold weather having apparently set in in earnest.

Oct.25   Very stormy morning, only 63 children present.

Nov. 9   Commenced Decimal fractions with Standard VI during the week.

Nov. 22   School examined in Religious Knowledge by Rev. A.J.Davidson. There were 107 children present. School closed for the remainder of the day.

Dec.20   Broke up this morning for the Christmas Holidays.

Jan. 7   Reopened school this morning.

Jan. 14   The pipes in Standard II and III room will not heat. The pipes were short of water through a leak in the cistern.

Jan. 25   Average reduced by seven this week through sickness.

Jan. 28   Only 53 children present this morning owing to the depth of snow lying on the ground.

Jan. 29   More snow during the night. 28 children present - closed for remainder of the week.

Feb. 11   Found the pipes frozen in the room occupied by Standard II and III.

Feb. 15   26 Scholars have been absent all week suffering from mumps. The average for the week is 61.

Feb. 26   Shrove Tuesday. Marked registers at 9 o'clock. Closed at 11 for the day.

Feb. 27   Ash Wednesday. Children went to service in church instead of Scripture Lesson.

© Topical Resources. May be photocopied for classroom use only.

March 15   *Commenced Vulgar Fractions with Standard V. Taught new song during singing lesson.*

March 16   *A photographer took the likenesses of the children this morning.*

April 8   *The time-table for the morning sessions during Passion Week will be as follows:*

> *9.10*   *Prayers and registers*
> *9.45*   *Arithmetic*
> *10.00*   *Spelling*
> *10.30*   *Reading*
> *11.10*   *Writing*

          This is in order to allow children to attend Divine Service in church.

April 11   *Closed at noon until Tuesday morning for Easter Holidays.*

April 16   *Reopened this morning.*

April 19   *Have not made up the fires after commencement of school this week.*

May 20   *School examined in drawing this afternoon by Mr. Wadeson. 53 children (boys) present.*

May 23   *Ascension day. Children went to service in church instead of Scripture lesson.*

May 31   *Gave out notice to children that all must be present on Tuesday morning for the examination.*

June 4   *School examined by D.Bostock Esq. H.M.I.. of schools. After exam closed for the week.*

June 10   *Opened school. Admitted 23 from the Infant school.*

June 17   *Gave out tickets for the Treat which will be held on Saturday.*

June 28   *Taught children music to a new song "Try Again" from the "Strand Music magazine" during singing lessons of this week.*

June 29   *The attendance this afternoon has been affected by a smart thunder shower during the dinner hour.*

July 5   *Report: The school has passed a fair examination in the elementary subjects in Geography, Answering on the Reading lessons, Handwriting on Paper. Spelling in the II and IV Standards and Mental arithmetic throughout are weak points. English, Needlework and Singing by note are good and order is well maintained.*

July 11   *Broke up this morning for Midsummer Holidays.*

© Topical Resources. May be photocopied for classroom use only.

School Rules

Rules for Children 1848

The following misbehaviours will be punished in the following ways:

(1) Playing cards at school
    10 lashes

(2) Swearing at school
    8 lashes

(3) Drinking liquor in school
    8 lashes

(4) Telling lies
    7 lashes

(5) Boys/Girls playing together
    4 lashes

(6) Quarelling
    2 lashes

(7) Wearing long fingernails
    2 lashes

(8) Blotting one's copy book
    2 lashes

(9) Neglecting to bow when going home
    2 lashes

Rules for Teachers 1872

(1) Teachers each day will fill lamps and clean chimneys.

(2) Each teacher will bring a bucket of water and a scuttle of coal for the day's session.

(3) Make your pens carefully. You may whittle nibs to the individual tastes of the pupils.

(4) Men teachers may take one evening a week for courting purposes or two evenings per week if they go to church regularly.

(5) After ten hours in school, the teacher may spend the remaining time reading the Bible or other good books.

(6) Women teachers who marry or engage in unseemly conduct will be dismissed.

(7) Every teacher shall lay aside from each pay a goodly sum of his earnings for his benifit during his declining years so that he will not become a burden on society.

(8) Any teacher who smokes, uses liquor in any form, frequents pool or public halls, or gets shaved in a barbers shop will have good reason to suspect his worth, intention, integrity and honesty.

(9) The teacher who performs his labour faithfully and without fail for five years will be given an increase of 25 cents per week in his pay, provided the Board of Education approves.

© Topical Resources. May be photocopied for classroom use only.

School Log Book
Questions to Answer

Every school has a book called a "Log Book". This is a book that the law requires the Headteacher to keep listing the main events that happen in the school . You would not be allowed to look in a recent Log Book because it may tell you things about people you know that used to attend the school but you are allowed to look at Log Books that were written many years ago.

Find a copy of " A Selection of Entries from the School Log Book of a Village National School July 1894 - July 1895". Read through this list of some of the events that happened over the course of one school year and answer the following questions:

(1)   Are there any events mentioned in these Log Book entries that would be unlikely to happen in your school now?
        If yes, list what they are and give your reasons for suggesting they are unlikely to happen now.

(2)   Why do you think the farmer's children would be away from school for a week in August?

(3)   How do you think the school was heated? What evidence suggests this?

(4)   Look at the morning time-table for April 8th. Which of these subjects do you study today? What subjects do you study that the children in this school did not? Why do you think this is? Are any subjects the same but now called by a different name?

(5)   What is a likeness?
        What is a school attendance officer?

(6)   In what ways might life in this school in 1894 be better than life in school today? In what ways might it be worse?

(7)   Did the children at this school have more or less holidays than children at school today.
        How did you work this out?

(8)   How do you know that a lot of people went home for their lunch?
        Why do you think this is?

School Rules
Questions to Answer

Schools in Victorian Times were very different from schools to-day. The classes were much larger, the children sat in rows facing the front and discipline was very strict indeed.

Study the document called "School Rules" and answer the following questions:

(1)   When were the "Rules for Children" written?
        How long ago is that?

(2)   What kinds of misbehaviour are not allowed in school to-day?

(3)   What "punishments" do you suffer if you do misbehave?

(4)   Do you think it is important to have rules for children?
        Why?

(5)   When were the "Rules for Teachers" written?
        How long ago is that?

(6)   How were the schools heated and lit?

(7)   Explain what Teachers Rule 8 means.

(8)   How many hours a day did a teacher have to spend in school?

(9)   How much time off could a male teacher have?

(10)   Can you think of any rules teachers have to obey to-day?

(11)   Now think sensibly! What rules would you like to add to the teachers list?
        Why?

(12)   These school rules came from America. What evidence can you find to prove this?

© Topical Resources. May be photocopied for classroom use only.

FACT or OPINION?

Sometimes it is difficult to say whether someone is telling the truth or not.
If someone tells you something it may be a **FACT** or they may be telling you
their **OPINION**.

FACT: a thing known to be true; a reality

OPINION: what one thinks about something; belief, judgement

On a separate piece of paper make a list of 5 FACTS about your school and 5
OPINIONS about your school. Sometimes it is hard to tell the difference isn't it?

Look at the sentences below. Are they **FACTS** or someone's **OPINION**?

1.   Queen Victoria reigned for 64 years.
2.   Teachers should not have been able to cane their pupils, it was cruel.
3.   Queen Victoria was the best Queen Britain has ever had.
4.   The suffragettes believed that women should have been able to vote..
5.   Florence Nightingale was a famous nurse who lived during Victorian
      Times.
6.   The railways were a good idea because even poorer people could
      afford to travel at a penny per mile.
7.   It was unfair that the British should rule over lots of other countries around
      the world who were part of the British Empire.
8.   In 1870 a law was passed which said that all children between the ages
      of 5 and 13 must go to school.
9.   A lot of changes took place in Britain during Victorian Times.
10.   Conditions in the workhouse were not too bad - the families who were
      looked after were lucky to have a roof over their heads.

Complete this table by putting the numbers under the correct heading:

FACT	OPINION

Can you make your own list of 5 facts and 5 opinions about Victorian Times
for a friend to put in a table?

© Topical Resources. May be photocopied for classroom use only.

Cause and Consequence

What caused this?

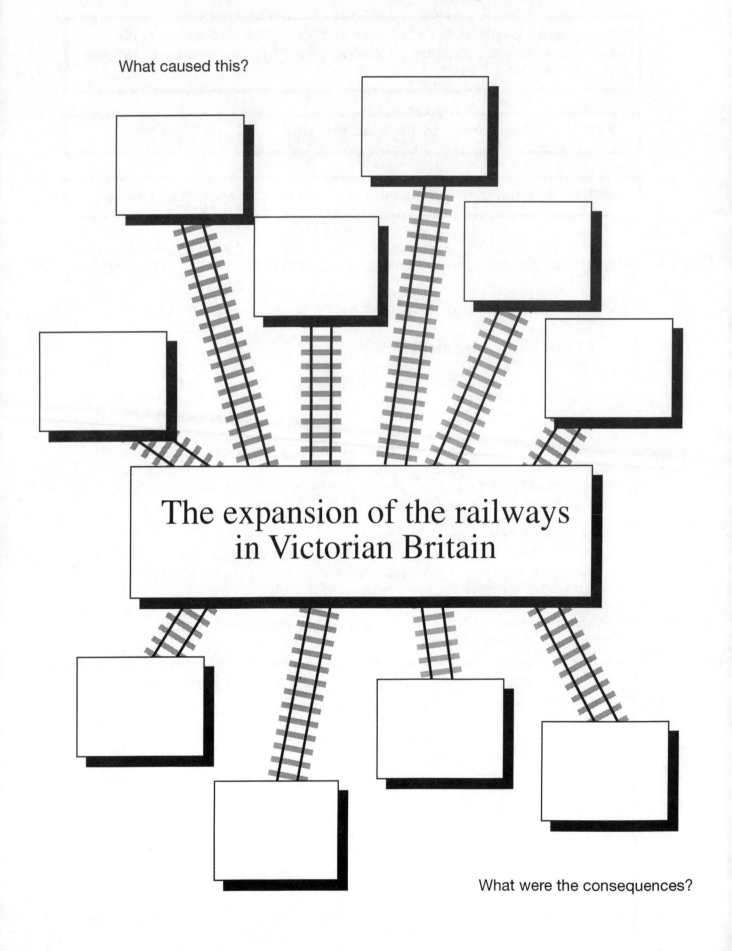

The expansion of the railways in Victorian Britain

What were the consequences?

© Topical Resources. May be photocopied for classroom use only.

A Victorian Britain Timeline:

In the circles below are events that took place in Britain during the reign of Queen Victoria.

Cut them out and place them in order on your Victorian Britain timeline.

If you research any other important inventions, events, or people of the Victorian era, add them to your timeline as you go along.

Be careful! Some of the circles does not contain dates - you will need to research these dates before you can add these facts to your timeline!

Dr Barnardo founds a charity 1866

Telephone invented

Alice in Wonderland written

Dunlop's Air-filled Tyres 1888

Snooker invented in1875

The Great Exhibition

Child Labour Law 1874

First wireless signal across Atlantic 1901

Zips introduced to Britain 1893

Crimean War

Victoria and Albert marry

Red Flag Law abolished

1889 Ewbank sweeper invented

Penny Post 1840

1841 Thomas Cook TravelAgency opens

Prince Albert dies 1861

Can you find out any more information about one or more of these facts?

© Topical Resources. May be photocopied for classroom use only.

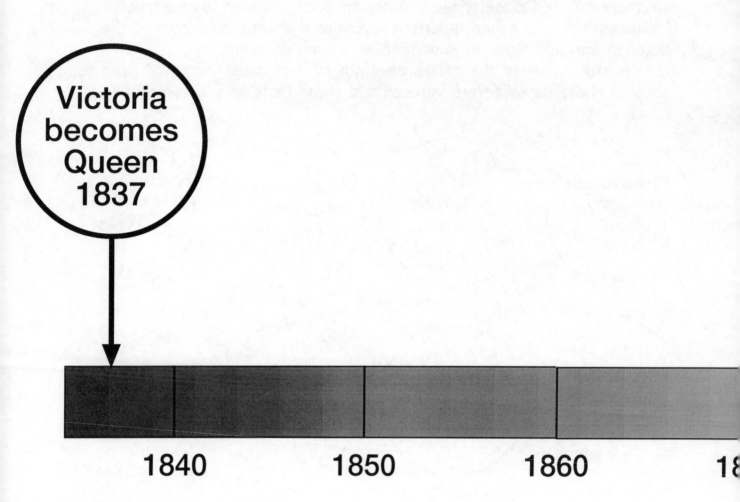

Victoria
becomes
Queen
1837

1840   1850   1860   18

© Topical Resources. May be p

N TIME LINE

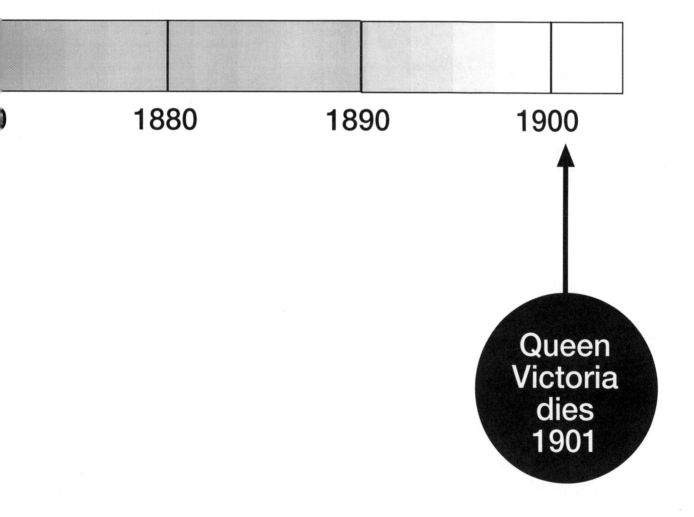

1880   1890   1900

Queen
Victoria
dies
1901

copied for classroom use only.

Evidence from old Photographs

This photograph shows a street in Preston, Lancashire. It was taken close to the end of the Victorian period. It shows a number of weavers cottages known locally as "Step Cottages" so called because of the steps up to the main entrance. This is where a weaver and his family would have lived. The hand loom was kept in the cellar. In poorer times as many as three families would share a house like this with looms also found on other floors.

Look at the photograph carefully and use your observations to answer the following questions:

(1)   Look carefully at the road surface. What is it made from? How is it different from todays roads? Why do you think streets are no longer made like this?

(2)   What sort of road transport can you see being used in this photograph?
       What do you think this sort of transport could be used for?
       What would you say was the modern version of this vehicle?

(3)   Look carefully towards the end of the street to find the street light.
       What do think powered this street light? Why?

(4)   Look at how the boy is dressed towards the front of the photograph.
       Compare this picture with reference books showing Victorian fashion.
       What does this tell you about this photograph?

(5)   Each house has a set of railings close to the cellar window.
       Why do you think this is?

(6)   How does the traffic in this photograph compare with the traffic found in streets today?
       Can you spot a cause of traffic pollution in the photograph which is no longer a problem today?

© Topical Resources. May be photocopied for classroom use only.

Evidence from old Photographs

This photograph was taken close to the end of the Victorian period. It shows an old lady sitting in her front room keeping warm by the range. She is sitting on a bed that has been brought downstairs for her because she has not been feeling so well. Her clothes are drying on the "clothes horse" or "maiden" to her left hand side next to the end of her bed.

Look at the photograph carefully and use your observations to answer the following questions:

(1)   The range was used for a number of different jobs. Use reference books to find out what some of these were.
        Do you think a room heated in this way would be comfortable to live in? Why?

(2)   Above the range there is a light fastened to the wall.
        How do you think this works?

(3)   How is this lady drying her washing? How do you dry your washing at home
        (a) when the weather is fine (b) when the weather is wet?
        What problems occur when drying the washing inside?

(4)   Name some of the objects on the mantelpiece.
        Why could young children not get at these?

(5)   If this lady was living in Victorian Times do you think she would be considered very poor, very wealthy or somewhere inbetween.
        What are your reasons for your answer?

(6)   How is the picture on the wall held up? Can you hang pictures in your own house in this way? If not, why not?
        If you can, try to find out when your house was built. Is it from Victorian Times?

© Topical Resources. May be photocopied for classroom use only.

Evidence from Period Drawings

Even though steam tractors had been invented it wasn't until the end of Victorian Times that they were a common sight on farms. Most small farms still relied on the traditional ways of farming as shown in these drawings from the period. Study these sketches and carefully draw your own modern version of each activity. You may need to use reference books to find out how a modern farm works.

© Topical Resources. May be photocopied for classroom use only.

Different Interpretations of the same Event

Feeding the poor at a Soup Kitchen during hard times in Victorian Preston.

(1)　Look carefully at the lady picking up a pan third from the front of the picture.
　　　Try to imagine the thoughts going through her head.
　　　Write a few sentences which show what she may be thinking.

_____

_____

_____

_____

_____

(2)　Find the fine gentleman wearing a top hat standing behind the soup kitchen counter.
　　　What do you believe he is thinking? Write a few sentences which tell of his thoughts.

_____

_____

_____

_____

_____

(3)　Why do you think these two people will think differently about the situation they find
　　　themselves in?

_____

_____

_____

_____

_____

Whenever you are looking at evidence - THINK: 'Whose evidence is this? Is it reliable?

© Topical Resources. May be photocopied for classroom use only.

Evidence from Newspaper Advertisements

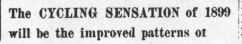

The CYCLING SENSATION of 1899 will be the improved patterns of

First in 1888, Foremost ever since.

DUNLOP TYRES

Upon receipt of a post-card we will register your address, and forward our illustrated descriptive booklet immediately upon its completion.

THE DUNLOP PNEUMATIC TYRE CO., LTD., 160 to 166, CLERKENWELL ROAD, LONDON, E.C.

THE "ENGLISH" ORGANETTE

Easy Payments. Only 4s. Monthly.
WITH EXPRESSION STOP.

Plays Hymns, Popular Airs, Quadrilles, Polkas, Waltzes, Hornpipes, &c. Any tune can be played with artistic effect by anyone. A mere child can play it. Most Marvellous Musical Instrument in the World.
Price 30s. Terms, 4s. Deposit and 4s. Monthly.
Organette delivered when first 4s. is paid.
Write for List of Music and Full Particulars.
(Mention this Paper.)
J. M. DRAPER, Organette Works, BLACKBURN.

A JEWEL OF A PEN.
3/-
Gold Mounted and Chased, 5/-
"CALTON"

The "CALTON" Stylographic Pen is the simplest and cheapest, and is praised by all who use it. We send it complete in Box, with Filler and Directions, post paid for 3/-
"JEWEL" FOUNTAIN PEN, fitted with 16-ct. Gold Nib, Iridium Tipped, 5/- Mounted and Chased, 7/6. All kinds repaired.
Dept. P. JEWEL PEN COMPANY,
58, FENCHURCH STREET, LONDON, E.C.

D'ALMAINE'S
PIANOS FROM 12 GS.
ORGANS FROM 5 GS.

Every Instrument warranted for ten years. Carriage Free on approval. Easy Terms. Full price paid will be allowed within three years if exchanged for a higher class Instrument.

D'ALMAINE & CO. (Estab. 112 Years), 91, Finsbury Pavement, E.C.

'ATLAS' LOCK-STITCH SEWING-MACHINE.
Equal in size and quality to any Machine. The best and cheapest for every use. Works by hand or treadle. Four years' guarantee. To ensure satisfaction we will send Machine on receipt of 5s. P.O. for ONE MONTH'S TRIAL, and if desired balance can be paid 5s. MONTHLY.
39/-
Call or write for Designs and Samples of Work.
THE 'ATLAS' MACHINE COMPANY,
182, HIGH STREET, CAMDEN TOWN, LONDON;
63, Seven Sisters Road, N.; and 14, High Road, Kilburn, N.W.

THE "OKTIS" CORSET SHIELDS
DOUBLE THE LIFE OF YOUR CORSET

PATENT

1/0½ PER PAIR, FROM YOUR DRAPER OR OUTFITTER
SEE THAT YOU GET "OKTIS"

Some people are very particular about the exact tick of time when their existence commenced, and if

BORN

at midnight there is often a dispute about the right date of the birth, owing to the discrepancies in the Watches and Clocks in the house. But

AT

last that difficulty is surmounted by buying GRAVES'S WATCHES or CLOCKS—the accuracy of which is another great success of

SHEFFIELD!

They are perfect specimens of sound workmanship, absolutely correct timekeepers, and everyone can buy them on the specially easy system of payment on which they are supplied.

SEE CATALOGUE. Sent free to any address on receipt of Post Card.

AGENTS WANTED FOR THE SALE OF

J. G. GRAVES'S
Watches, Clocks, & Jewellery.
PLEASE WRITE FOR TERMS.
DIVISION STREET, SHEFFIELD.

The Victorian Times saw enormous growth in the production of newspapers especially after the mid 1850's.

This was due to improvements in the printing process, the ease of distribution using railways and changes in tax on advertisements. The prices of papers fell from 7d at the beginning of the century to 1/2d by the end. As more and more people learnt to read through going to school the demand for newspapers grew. These advertisements have been taken from an 1898 newspaper. They show advertisements for everyday things used by the people who lived in these times.

Use the information in these advertisements to help you to answer the following questions:

(1)   What was Dunlop first with in 1888?

(2)   What is the "English Organette" used for?
What would be the modern version of this device?

(3)   Do you think many people would buy the pen shown in the advertisement? Give your reasons for your answer.

(4)   How much is 1 guinea worth today? What is the modern price for the cheapest piano shown in the advertisement? How much would the cheapest organ cost today?

(5)   What do you think "Equal in size and quality to any machine" means in the sewing machine advertisement?

(6)   What is the purpose of "The Oktis Corset Shield" ? Why do you think ladies would want to buy such a device?

(7)   What is being sold in the advertisement with the large letters BORN AT SHEFFIELD? Describe the product in detail. Try to find out why this was "another great success of Sheffield".

© Topical Resources. May be photocopied for classroom use only.

Evidence from Newspaper Advertisements

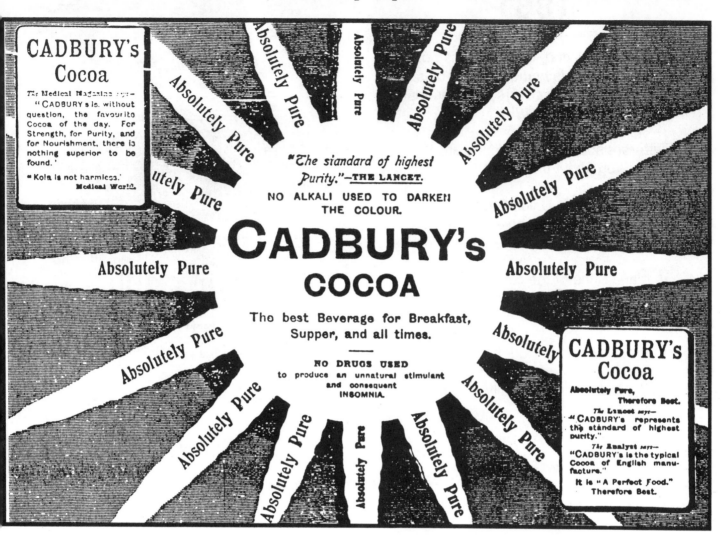

BIRD'S CUSTARD POWDER

When the Pie was opened,
The birds began to sing—
The Praises of Bird's Custard Powder.

The Unfailing Resource of every Lady of the House and successful Housekeeper.

Makes a perfect high-class Custard at a minimum of cost and trouble. Used by all the leading Diplomées of the South Kensington School of Cookery. Invaluable also for a variety of Sweet Dishes, recipes for which accompany each packet.

NO EGGS! NO RISK! NO TROUBLE!

These advertisements are taken from a paper published in 1898.

1. Design a modern-day advert for one of these products.

   How will you change the wording? illustration? style of lettering? Why does it need changing?

2. Look in magazines and try to find a modern advertisement for a similar product. Draw up a list of all the things that are the same as this advert and all the things that are different.

39

© Topical Resources. May be photocopied for classroom use only.

Union Street 1861

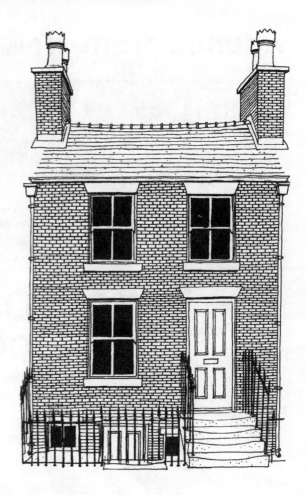

Union Street in Leyland, Lancashire is now called Fox Lane and is home to a row of 'step-houses' or hand-loom weavers cottages that appear in the Census for 1861.

Three different sources of evidence are provided for you about this street:

A   Photographs of Union Street. One taken towards the end of the Victorian period and one taken recently.

B   A plan of one of the cottages on Union Street showing the ground floor, the first floor, the cellar and the attic.

C   Census returns for four houses on Union Street in 1861, giving you information about four families who lived in these houses.

To complete this task you will need copies of all the source material listed above:

Source Sheet A: Photographs
Source Sheet B: Plans
Source Sheet C: Census Returns

1   Choose one of the four families listed in the Census Returns.
2   Compile a 'Family Dossier' about your Victorian Family. (e.g. a booklet or loose-leaf folder) and include the following:

    a   A front cover.
    b   A sketch of their house based on the artist's impression above and the plans and photographs in Source Sheets A and B.
    c   A Family Portrait (don't forget to research clothing in 1861 for a working class family!).
    d   A Family Tree.
    e   A Family Timeline.
    f   A page for each family member in turn giving as much detail as you can find out (or guess) about;
         - conditions at their place of work.
         - their view of life
         - their life so far
         - their relationships with other members of their family and home life
         - other details that you would like to add!

WARNING: Which bits of your family dossier are based on actual evidence?
Which bits are made up or have you had to make a guess about?
Bear this in mind when you are presented with anybody's interpretation of History.
How much is fact? How much is guess work?

© Topical Resources. May be photocopied for classroom use only.

SOURCE SHEET A: Photographs

Here are two photographs of Union Street
(now called Fox Lane) in Leyland, Lancashire.
The first was taken in the late 1800s and the second was
taken recently from the same place.
Although many changes have taken place a lot is still the same,
including the weavers' cottages to the left of the photo.

© Topical Resources. May be photocopied for classroom use only.

SOURCE SHEET B: Plans

These are the plans of the cellar, ground floor, first floor and attic of one of the weavers' cottages on Union Street.

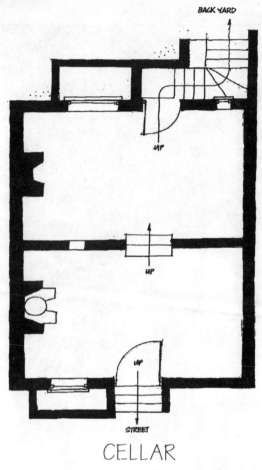

CELLAR

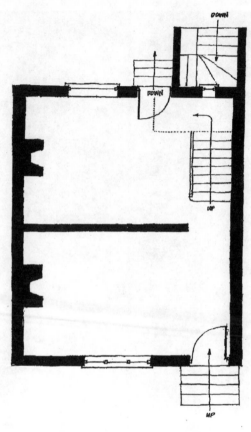

GROUND FLOOR

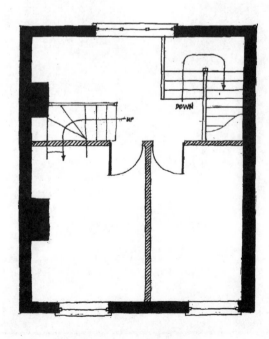

FIRST FLOOR

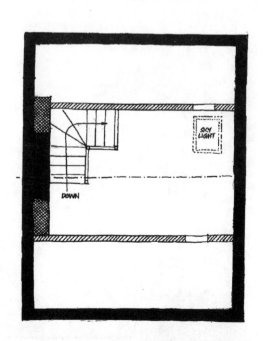

ATTIC

© Topical Resources. May be photocopied for classroom use only.

SOURCE SHEET C: Census Returns for Union Street

This is an extract from the 1861 Census for Union Street, Leyland, Lancashire.

Can you find out how often Census Information is collected? Why is it kept secret for 100 years?

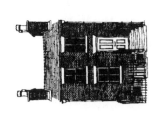

STREET	NUMBER	SURNAME	FORENAMES	POSITION	AGE	OCCUPATION	BIRTHPLACE	COMMENTS
Union Street	Number 17	Baron	Richard	Head	56 years	Clogger	Leyland	
		Baron	Issabella	Wife	50 years		Leyland	
		Baron	Thomas	Son	17 years	Clamper, Bleachworks	Leyland	
		Baron	Elizabeth	Daughter	15 years	Dressmaker's Apprentice	Leyland	Deaf & Dumb
		Baron	Samuel	Son	12 years	Scholar	Leyland	
		Baron	Prudence	Daughter	9 years	Scholar	Leyland	
		Baron Rose	James	Wife's son	28 years	Packer, Bleachworks	Leyland	
	Number 26	Norris	Ellen	Head	62 years		Leyland	
		Norris	Margaret	Daughter	39 years	Grey marker, Bleachworks	Leyland	
		Norris	Dorothy	Daughter	31 years	Grey sticker, Bleachworks	Leyland	
		Norris	Margaret	Grand daughter	11 years	Scholar	Leyland	
		Nixon	James	Visitor	36 years	Labourer, Spinning Mill	Pendleton	
		Jackson	George	Lodger	27 years	Book-keeper	Withington	
	Number 47	Hatch	Oliver	Head	43 years	Crofter, Bleachworks	Adlington	
		Hatch	Mary	Wife	41 years		Blackrod	
		Hatch	Moses	Son	15 years	Blaterdown, Bleachworks	Anderton	
		Hatch	Robert	Son	9 years	Scholar	Adlington	
		Hatch	Sarah	Daughter	7 years	Scholar	Adlington	
		Hatch	Isaac	Son	5 years	Scholar	Adlington	
	Number 49	Beardwood	Robert	Head	42 years	Postman	Leyland	
		Beardwood	Catherine	Wife	42 years		Leyland	
		Beardwood	Joseph	Son	16 years	Crofter, Bleachworks	Leyland	
		Beardwood	James	Son	14 years	Crofter, Bleachworks	Leyland	
		Marsden	Daniel	Lodger	19 years	Gardener	Whittle-le-Woods	

© Topical Resources. May be photocopied for classroom use only.

Make a model step cottage

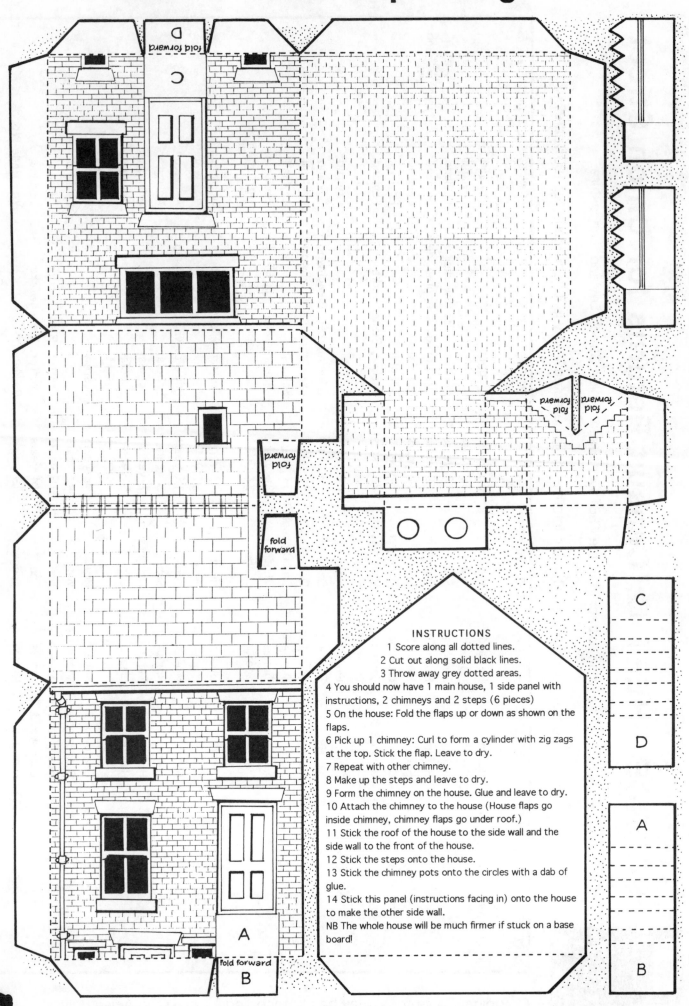

INSTRUCTIONS

1 Score along all dotted lines.

2 Cut out along solid black lines.

3 Throw away grey dotted areas.

4 You should now have 1 main house, 1 side panel with instructions, 2 chimneys and 2 steps (6 pieces)

5 On the house: Fold the flaps up or down as shown on the flaps.

6 Pick up 1 chimney: Curl to form a cylinder with zig zags at the top. Stick the flap. Leave to dry.

7 Repeat with other chimney.

8 Make up the steps and leave to dry.

9 Form the chimney on the house. Glue and leave to dry.

10 Attach the chimney to the house (House flaps go inside chimney, chimney flaps go under roof.)

11 Stick the roof of the house to the side wall and the side wall to the front of the house.

12 Stick the steps onto the house.

13 Stick the chimney pots onto the circles with a dab of glue.

14 Stick this panel (instructions facing in) onto the house to make the other side wall.

NB The whole house will be much firmer if stuck on a base board!

© Topical Resources. May be photocopied for classroom use only.

Using Literature as Evidence

Literature is another way that we can find out about the past.
The following passage is taken from a book called 'Her Benny' by Silas Hocking, written in Victorian times as a record of the life of poor children in Liverpool.

'Much to their relief, they found the house empty. A lump of coal was smouldering in the grate, which Benny at once broke up, and soon a ruddy glare from the fire lighted up the dismal room.

The furniture consisted of a three-legged round table, a chair minus a leg, and a three-legged stool. On the window-sill there was a glass bottle with a candle stuck in the neck, and under the stairs there was a heap of rags and shavings, on which Benny and his sister slept. A frying pan was suspended against the wall near the fireplace, and several cracked cups and saucers, together with a quart pint mug, stood on the table. The only other article of furniture was a small cupboard in a corner of the room close up to the ceiling, placed there, no doubt, to be out of the way of the children. Drawing the chair and stool close up to the fire, Benny and his sister waited the return of their parents.

Outside the wind moaned and wailed, and whistled through the keyhole and the chinks in the door, and rattled the paper and rags with which the holes in the window were stopped. And as the children listened they shivered, and drew closer together, and nearer the fire.'

Having read this extract, draw a picture of this scene in as much detail as you can:

45

© Topical Resources. May be photocopied for classroom use only.

Evidence from Interviews (Oral History)

"Yes we'd running water but only cold. There was no hot water in houses in them days, no baths or anything like that. We'd cold water and it was warmed in a boiler beside the fire... and all the water for washing had to be boiled... had to be heated. Some houses had no water. They went down to a pump and just got the water with a pump... They had all the water to carry into the houses."

Mrs Dutton (8.10.92)

In each water droplet write one job that has been done in your house this week that needs water:

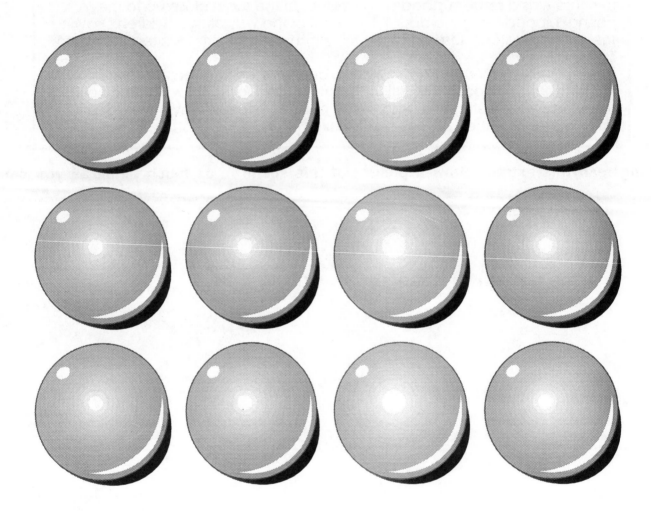

Colour all the jobs that need HOT water in red and all the jobs that need COLD water in blue

THINK

Why was it harder to do jobs around the house in Victorian Times?

What has made it easier for us today?

What can you find out about: COOKING or WASHING or HYGIENE in Victorian Britain?

Ask you teacher for a 'Victorian Britain Factsheet' to complete

© Topical Resources. May be photocopied for classroom use only.

Evidence from Interviews (Oral History)

"Q What was your house like when you were young?..........
A Well they weren't furnished like they are today: People hadn't the money, but we did our best, and they were always clean, but we didn't worry much........
Well they were flag floors but we had them covered with home-made rugs so they were warm."

Mrs Dutton (8.10.92)

How to make a rag rug

You will need:

A piece of jute scrim or open weave sacking approximately 30cm x 30 cm (available from T.T.S. Educational Catalogue and other suppliers)
Scraps of material

What to do:

1   Cut strips of scrap material about 1cm wide and 20cm long.

2   Loop into a 'U' shape

3   Push the closed end through gaps in the jute material and feed open ends through the loop.

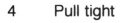

4   Pull tight

5   Repeat the process, keeping loops as close together as possible.

6   Finish by trimming loose ends to all the same length.

Better still why not invite a local crafts worker or grandparent in to show you how it's done!

© Topical Resources. May be photocopied for classroom use only.

Conditions in the Mills: Part 1

The Weaving is a trade Boys that never can fail,
As long as folks need clothes to keep one another hail,
So let us all be merry and drink this good ale,
And drink to the health of the Weavers.

" Conditions in my mill are as good as many, and better than most.
Sober, steady men can expect to be well trained and earn one guinea weekly, clear to themselves.
I provide constant employment for anyone over 9 years of age. A tolerable good spinner can with ease earn from 30 to 40 shillings per week, clear.
I provide secure jobs, a good wage and all the latest machinery. It is a pleasure to work in my mill."

Having read the evidence from Mr. Simpson, a mill owner from Lancashire in the 19th Century, how would you feel about working in his mill?

Herbert Simpson
Mill owner

Draw your own picture of Mr. Simpson

_____
_____
_____
_____
_____
_____
_____
_____
_____
_____
_____
_____
_____

48

© Topical Resources. May be photocopied for classroom use only.

Conditions in the Mills: Part 2

" I am a runaway. I left the weaving shed where I was an apprentice without permission because I couldn't stand the conditions any longer. In Preston recently, a boy lost his head in machinery. The bosses don't care they are only interested in lots of profit and long hours for little pay.

The watchman at Bannister Hall Print works lost his arm in an explosion and you hear about fires in factories all the time.

I know I have broken the law, and anyone who hides me will also be severely punished. I heard of a boy who was sent to sea for stealing a bushel of Oats. Some people are transported for seven years. I'm scared but I can't work in those conditions for another day."

Having read the evidence from Betty Sumner, how would you now feel about working in this mill?

Betty Sumner
Mill worker

Draw your own picture of Betty

_____
_____
_____
_____
_____
_____
_____
_____
_____
_____
_____
_____
_____
_____
_____

© Topical Resources. May be photocopied for classroom use only.

Make a Zoetrope

Instructions

1   Photocopy pages 50 and 51 and stick them on black paper.
2   Cut out the circular base by cutting along the solid black line.
3   Cut out the three strips on the page by cutting along the solid black lines. Remember to leave the tabs on!
4   Score and fold along the dotted lines.
5   Stick the side flaps behind as marked to make a ring, with the pictures facing the inside of the circle.
6   Fold the bottom flaps inside the circle and dab them with glue.
7   Push the circle down inside the ring and stick it onto the flaps - like putting the bottom in a cake-tin!
8   Push a drawing pin down through the centre of the base into a plastic pop bottle with water in to weigh it down.
9   Spin the ring quickly and look at the pictures through the slots. See the image appear to move!!

© Topical Resources. May be photocopied for classroom use only.

stick behind C · A

stick behind A · B

stick behind B · C

© Topical Resources. May be photocopied for classroom use only.

Now & *Then* Pairs

The Artefacts matching game

A game for 2-4 players.
Cut out these pictures of Victorian and Modern household objects to make a set of 26 cards.
Turn them over and mix them up.
One player pick up two cards.
If the Victorian artefact matches the modern artefact you may keep the pair and have another go.
If not, put the cards back and let the next person have a go.
The winner is the player with the most pairs at the end!

© Topical Resources. May be photocopied for classroom use only.

Now & *Then* Pairs

The Artefacts matching game

For a full set of instructions see Page 52

© Topical Resources. May be photocopied for classroom use only.

Transport in Victorian Times

In Victorian times people walked a lot more than we do today.

Vans, carts and buses were pulled by horses. Even taxis called Hansom Cabs used horses.

The first railway was opened in 1825. After this railways spread all over the country.

The first bicycles were invented. The penny farthing was popular but dangerous to ride.

Most ships used sails but many were fitted with steam engines. The first metal ships were made.

In 1885 a German called Benz built the first motor car which used a petrol engine.

(1) In Victorian Times people _____ a lot more than we do today.

(2) Vans, _____ and _____ were pulled by horses. Even taxis called

Hansom Cabs used _____

(3) The first _____ was opened in 1825. After this _____

spread all over the country.

(4) The first _____ were invented. The _____ farthing was

popular but dangerous to ride.

(5) Most ships used _____ but many were fitted with steam _____

The first metal ships were made.

(6) In 1885 a German called _____ built the first motor car which used a petrol

engine.

(7) Carefully draw and colour your own picture of some Victorian people travelling.

Level 2 - Topical Resources - May be photocopied for classroom use only

Transport in Victorian Times

In Victorian Times people walked a lot more than we do today. The streets in towns and cities would be filled with vans, carts and buses pulled by horses. In London wealthy people used a sort of horse drawn taxi called a Hansom cab. The first railway was opened to the public in 1825. After this event railways were built all over the country and even the less well off could now travel long distances. The first bicycles were invented the Penny Farthing being very popular for a time. Ships were beginning to be fitted with steam engines making them faster than sailing ships. The first metal ships were made. In 1885 a German called Benz built the first motor car which used a petrol engine.

A (1) What could be seen in the streets of the towns and cities?

(2) How did wealthy London people travel ?

(3) When was the first public railway opened?

(4) What is a Penny Farthing?

(5) What made ships travel more quickly?

(6) When was the first motor car built?

(7) What sort of engine did the first motor car use?

B (1) Why do you think Victorian people walked more than we do?

(2) Why do you think railways were built all over the country?

C Carefully draw and colour your own picture of Victorian people travelling.

Transport in Victorian Times

In Victorian Times people walked a lot more than we do today. The streets in towns and cities would be filled with vans, carts and buses pulled by horses. In London wealthy people used a sort of horse drawn taxi called a Hansom cab. Horse drawn traffic jams in London resulted in the construction of the world's first underground railway. Steam trains were used but were soon replaced by cleaner electric trains. The very first public railway was opened in 1825. The first train was pulled by George Stevenson's Locomotion. After this event railways were built all over the country and even the less well off could now travel long distances. The first bicycles were invented, the Penny Farthing being very popular for a time. The Rover Safety Bicycle was the first to look like bicycles of today. Ships were beginning to be fitted with steam engines making them faster than sailing ships. The first metal ships were made. In 1885 a German called Benz built the first motor car which used a petrol engine. By the end of the century people travelled much more than ever before.

A (1) What could be seen in the streets of the towns and cities?

  (2) How did wealthy London people travel?

  (3) Why was an underground railway built in London?

  (4) When was the first public railway opened?

  (5) What is a Penny Farthing?

  (6) What made ships travel more quickly?

  (7) Who built the first motor car?

B (1) Why do you think Victorian people walked more than we do?

  (2) Why do you think electric trains were used on the underground railway?

  (3) Why do you think railways were built all over the country?

  (4) Do you think bicycles would be popular in Victorian Times? Why?

  (5) Did people travel more at the end of Victorian Times? Why?

C Carefully draw, colour and label several pictures which show different types of transport used in Victorian Times.

Transport in Victorian Times

In Victorian Times people walked a lot more than we do today as very few people owned their own transport and many could not even afford to travel by public transport. However, things changed considerably during the time Victoria was on the throne. The streets in towns and cities filled up with vans, carts and buses pulled by horses. In London wealthy people used a sort of horse drawn taxi called a Hansom cab. Horse drawn traffic jams in London resulted in the construction of the worlds first underground railway. Steam trains were used but were soon replaced by cleaner electric trains. The very first public railway was opened in 1825. The first train was pulled by George Stevenson's Locomotion. After this event railways were built all over the country. Soon nearly every town and village had a railway station and even the less well off could travel long distances. The first bicycles were invented, the Penny Farthing being very popular for a time. This was a bicycle with one very large wheel at the front and a much smaller one behind. Penny Farthings could travel at some speed but were extremely dangerous to ride. The Rover Safety Bicycle was the first to look like bicycles of today. Ships were beginning to be fitted with steam engines making them faster than sailing ships although it was some time before they began to rival the Clippers on their long journeys to China and Australia. The first metal ships were made. In 1885 a German called Benz built the first motor car which used a petrol engine. By the end of the century people travelled much more than ever before.

A (1) What could be seen in the streets of the towns and cities?
  (2) How did wealthy London people travel?
  (3) Why was an underground railway built in London?
  (4) When were railways built all over the country?
  (5) Why do you think a Penny Farthing would be dangerous to ride?
  (6) What made ships travel more quickly?
  (7) Where did "Clippers" journey to?
  (8) Who built the first motor car?

B (1) Do you think bicycles would be popular in Victorian Times? Why?
  (2) Why do you think railways were built all over the country?
  (3) How do you think the Penny Farthing got its name?
  (4) Why did people travel more at the end of Victorian Times?

C Use reference books to research:
  (1) "Clippers"
  (2) The "first metal ships" or the "first motor cars".

Carefully illustrate your work.

Level 5 - Topical Resources - May be photocopied for classroom use only.

The Work of Florence Nightingale

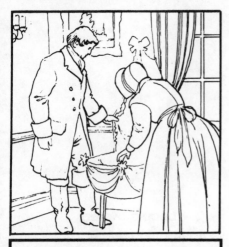

Florence Nightingale was born to rich parents who were on holiday in Italy.

She did not go to school. Instead she was taught at home by a governess.

When she grew up she wanted to help the poor and sick people she had seen on her travels.

She went to Germany to train to be a nurse.

She nursed British soldiers that were ar war. She made the hospitals much cleaner.

Later she taught others what to do and many hospitals became healthier places.

(1) Florence Nightingale was born to _____ parents who were on _____ in Italy.

(2) She did not go to school. Instead she was taught at _____ by a governess.

(3) When she grew up she wanted to help the _____ and _____ people she had seen on her travels.

(4) She went to Germany to train to be a _____ .

(5) She nursed British soldiers that were at _____ . She made the hospitals much cleaner.

(6) Later she _____ others what to do and many _____ became healthier places.

(7) Carefully draw and colour your own picture of Florence Nightingale at work.

The Work of Florence Nightingale

Florence Nightingale was born to rich parents who were on a long holiday in Italy. She did not go to school. Instead she was taught at home by a governess. When she grew up she wanted to help the poor and sick people she had seen on her travels but her parents were not keen to let her do this. She went to Germany to train to be a nurse. Her first job was looking after gentlewomen in a home. She was shocked at how dirty the place was and started to clean up straight away. She organised hot water and properly cooked meals. She taught the other nurses the importance of keeping things clean. Her next job was nursing British soldiers that were at war. After this she taught other people about nursing and as a result many hospitals became healthier places.

A (1) Did Florence Nightingale go to school?

   (2) What did she want to do when she grew up?

   (3) Where did she train to be a nurse?

   (4) What was her first job?

   (5) What was it that shocked her?

   (6) What was her next job?

   (7) What did she teach other people?

B (1) Why do you think her parents did not want Florence to become a nurse?

   (2) Why do you think many hospitals became healthier places?

C Carefully draw and colour your own picture of Florence at work.

Level 3 - Topical Resources - May be photocopied for classroom use only.

The Work of Florence Nightingale

Florence Nightingale was born to rich parents during a long holiday in Italy. She did not go to school, instead she was taught at home by a governess. When she grew up she wanted to help the poor and sick people she had seen on her travels but her parents were not keen to let her do this. She went to Germany to train to be a nurse as proper training was not available in this country. Her first job was looking after gentlewomen in a home. She was shocked at how dirty the place was and started to clean up straight away. She organised hot water and properly cooked meals. She taught the other nurses the importance of keeping things clean. Her next job was nursing British soldiers injured in the Crimean war against Russia. The soldiers were dying more from disease than from bullet wounds. She set up a hospital in an old army barracks were the soldiers could be looked after in clean conditions. She walked the wards at night with her lamp. Afterwards she taught other people about nursing and as a result many hospitals became healthier places.

A (1) Did Florence Nightingale go to school?

(2) What did she want to do when she grew up?

(3) Why did she train to be a nurse in Germany?

(4) What was her first job?

(5) What was it that shocked her? What did she do about it?

(6) What was her next job?

(7) What did she teach other people?

B (1) What evidence suggests Florence came from a wealthy home?

(2) Why do you think her parents did not want Florence to become a nurse?

(3) Why do you think more soldiers were dying from disease than bullets?

(4) Why do you think Florence walked around the wards at night?

(5) Why do you think many hospitals became healthier places?

C Carefully draw and colour your own picture of Florence at work.

Level 4 - Topical Resources - May be photocopied for classroom use only.

The Work of Florence Nightingale

Florence Nightingale was born to rich parents in Italy whilst they were on a journey through Europe. They owned three houses. She did not go to school, instead she was taught at home by a governess. As she grew up she enjoyed all the privileges of wealth, going to the theatre, concerts and travelling abroad. One gentleman waited seven years to marry her but she would not agree. Eventually she decided she wanted to help the poor and sick people she had seen on her travels but her parents were not keen to let her do this. Hospitals were dirty places. No anaesthetics were used in operations and people died because wounds were not clean. She went to Germany to train to be a nurse as proper training was not available in this country. Her first job was looking after gentlewomen in a home. She was shocked at how dirty the place was and started to clean up straight away. She organised hot water and properly cooked meals. She taught the other nurses the importance of keeping things clean. Her next job was nursing British soldiers injured in the Crimean war against Russia. The soldiers were dying more from disease than from bullet wounds. She set up a hospital in an old army barracks were the soldiers could be looked after in clean conditions. She walked the wards at night with her lamp. Afterwards she conducted a campaign to improve medical care in the armed forces and in hospitals generally. She taught other people about nursing and as a result many hospitals became healthier places. Eventually she became ill and spent the rest of her life as an invalid.

A (1) Why did Florence Nightingale not go to school?

   (2) What good work did Florence decide she wanted to do?

   (3) Why did her parents not want her to become a nurse?

   (4) Why did she train to be a nurse in Germany?

   (5) What shocked her about her fist job? What did she do about this?

   (6) What was her second job?

   (7) How did she help the soldiers?

   (8) What did she teach other people about? Why did she do this?

B (1) Define the words: privilege; disease; barracks; campaign.

   (2) What evidence suggests Florence came from a wealthy home?

   (3) Why do you think more soldiers were dying from disease than bullets?

   (4) Why do you think Florence walked around the wards at night?

C Use reference books to research:

   (1) How the discovery of anaesthetics improved hospital operations.

   (2) How the work of Florence Nightingale improved nursing.

Carefully illustrate your work.

Level 5 - Topical Resources - May be photocopied for classroom use only.

Time to Spare Activities

1   Write a speech for Lord Shaftesbury to deliver in parliament about child labour.

2   Write a newspaper report of the above speech.

3   Design a modern newspaper advertisement for a Victorian invention (eg flat iron).

4   Research as much information as you can about Law & Order in Victorian Britain.

5   Research as much information as you can about Crime & Punishment in Victorian Britain.

6   Research as much information as you can about 'Votes for Women'.

7   Make a 'Votes for Women' banner and display in your classroom.

8   Write a letter of protest to the Prime Minister concerning votes for women.

9   Present an arguement for or against a new railway being built through your local community.

10 Research a victorian invention still in use today.

11 List equipment used in a modern kitchen and compare this with what was available in Victorian Times.

12 List all the jobs done by mothers in your class. Compare this with work carried out by women in Victorian Times.

13 List ten items typical of the period that you would include in a time-capsule created in 1894 and one created in 1994. How do they differ?

14 Research a famous Victorian personality.

15 Choose a year in Victorian Times and research as many facts or events as you can that happened in that year.

16 Make a large time-line to go on display in your classroom.

17 Sketch a Victorian artefact or part of an atrefact, using a view-finder.

18 Organise an 'Antiques Roadshow'! Invite parents and friends to participate and bring along Victorian items for the class to offer an 'expert' opinion on.

19 Choose an atrefact and think of a question about the past that this artefact helps to answer (eg stone hot water bottle - "How did people heat their beds before plastic was invented?").

20 Design and sew a Victorian Sampler.

21 Design and create a Victorian greetings card.

22 Make a collection of Victorian postcards.

23 Compare a Victorian OS map of your area with a modern equivalent.

24 Make a pin-hole camera.

25 Make a collection of Victorian photographs and disp;lay them in your classroom.

26 Research the first motor cars.

27 Research bicycles used in Victorian Times.

28 Make a model mine shaft with a working lift.

29 Use a fountain pen to write in 'copperplate' handwriting - careful!

30 Find out how to add pounds, shillings and pence.

31 Research why 'The sun never set on the British Empire' (clue: Find out about Time Zones first).

32 Research games children played in Victorian Times. Make one and teach a friend how to play it.

33 Collect modern Christmas Cards and sort ones with Victorian scenes.

34 Make a toy Victorian Theatre.

Notes for Teachers
on Photocopiable Worksheets & Activities:

Page   **Brief notes on use**

18   This map could be used as a simple information sheet **or** as source material and ask questions about it **or** give the children a blank map of the world and transfer the information onto it **or** give the children an atlas and ask them to name the countries that made up the Empire!

19   A self assessment activity to give to the children before any work is done on the topic and again at the end.

20   A useful chart to begin any History Study Unit with. Where does this period in History fit in? What came before? What came after? The children could put appropriate illustrations in the boxes by each time band **or** have this sheet with them in their Record of Achievement and evaluate each one as they do it! Alternatively this could go in the front of their folder and have the appropriate band coloured in to show where in History they are this term.

21   A stock of these in the classroom will enable you to give a research-based activity to any child finishing early or needing further study. Present the child with this sheet and ask them to research a particular aspect of Victorian Britain using reference materials in class and/or the school library. Also a good homework sheet.

22   An individual research activity that leads to a class display!

23   Here the onus is on the children to come up with the questions and realise that historical sources can help us to answer questions about the past.

24   This sheet contains an extract from Queen Victoria's personal diaries and calls for empathetic understanding and creative writing from the children.

25-26 Source sheets that can be used in any number of ways... Possible questions to answer are provided as a worksheet on Page 28.

27   Another source sheet, this time giving rules governing pupils and teachers during the reign of Queen Victoria. Again a worksheet based on these rules is to be found on page 28.

28   Two sets of questions based on the source materials presented on pages 25-27. The questions lead the children beyond simple comprehension and into making deductions and drawing parallels between the events of the past and the needs of today.

29   An activity that introduces the idea of Fact and Opinion, defines what is meant by this and uses both the child's own experience and aspects of life in Victorian Britain to teach the concept.

30   The children are asked to research and state 6 reasons why the railways expanded in Victorian Britain, and in turn explain 4 of the consequences of that expansion.

31-33 A time-line activity whereby the children are given a copy of the centre-page spread (a timeline of the Victorian period) and asked to cut out the facts in the circles and stick them in the correct place on the timeline. Some of the circles are deliberately without dates and will need researching. This could be the full extent of the activity but it could be expanded to include group research and presentations on different events mentioned in the timeline. As the term goes on the children could add their own facts to the timeline and build up a personalised version. This could also provide the basis for a large-scale timeline on display in the classroom.

34-35 At this stage the children are introduced to the idea of different types of evidence and pages 34 and 35 provide photographic evidence of life in a Northern industrial town at the end of the Victorian period. The pictures are accompanied by questions which encourage the children to look closely at the evidence provided and start to make deductions from what they are presented with. There is also scope to use the photos in different ways... (eg a picture of the old lady could form the basis for a teacher to go in role in Drama and tell the children about her life... the street photo could lead to research and sketches of Victorian, Edwardian and early 20th Century dress...)

36   Here the source material is woodcut sketches of the year of a farmer in Victorian Times. This sheet could also be used as part of a topic on the history of food and farming.

The children are asked to research the year on a modern farm and draw and/or describe the modern equivalent in the boxes provided. This could lead onto a farm visit or talk by a local farmer and memories of older members of the farming community of the tools and methods of yesteryear.

37 This activity introduces the children to the idea that evidence is different when collected from people with different viewpoints. They are asked to consider the differing opinions of people within the same setting and consider why this may be so. Work using modern day newspapers may help to emphasise this point. On a particular day buy a number of national newspapers and give the children the different front pages. Why do different newspapers give different stories prominence? How does their handling of the same story differ?

38-39 Here the children are provided with clippings from period newspapers and the uses of these sources are endless! The first sheet provides the children with questions to answer which draws their attention to the fine detail and small print and the second sheet extends this into relating the concept of advertising to modern day equivalents. The children are also asked to consider WHY these adverts are not necessarily appropriate today (eg emphasis on women in the kitchen... exaggerated claims... lack of eye-catching graphics etc...)

40-43 This four-page section is a self-contained project pack. It is based on a street of weavers (or step-) cottages and encourages the children to use the different sources to put together a dossier on a family that lived in that street in 1861. The pack includes a task sheet for the children and source sheets containing photographic evidence, an artists impression, plans of the house and census returns.

44 This activity sheet enables the children to make a model of one of the cottages mentioned in the project pack. It is advisable to photocopy this sheet onto card or ask the children to stick the photocopy onto card before they begin, for added strength. Scoring the dotted lines is all important and the house is designed so that a whole row of cottages can be coloured and stuck together. CAUTION! When colouring the house avoid paint which will make the card go soft. Coloured Pencil or pastel will provide a particularly good effect.

45 An introduction to the use of extracts

from literature as historical evidence. The children are asked to model a picture based on the passage.

46 Based on oral evidence from the interview with Mrs Dutton (Transcript pages 13-16) this sheet encourages the children to consider the uses of water in the home, whether this is hot or cold water, and the difficulty caused by not having hot running water. It also encourages them to research some aspects of domestic life in Victorian Britain further and for this copies of page 21 'Victorian Britain Factsheet' are required.

47 This sheet again draws on oral evidence but this time it is a practical activity whereby a group of children make a rag rug (or part of a class rug)!

48-49 Based on actual evidence (Betty Sumner really existed) these sheets develop the children's understanding of viewpoint and given one after the other enable them to see that there are two sides to every story. They also introduce the subject of factory conditions in this period of history which is an important aspect of this study unit.

50-51 A practical and fun activity - Make your own Zoetrope! The children are guided in the production of a simple devise to explain the basic principles behind moving pictures. Once again the structure is made much more solid if the sheets are photocopied onto card.

52-53 A matching pairs game that can be photocopied onto coloured card, cut up, laminated and played over and over again. The children build up an understanding of Now & Then and how domestic artefacts have developed and changed. An actual display of household artefacts from the period would reinforce this activity beautifully and lead to lots of excellent opportunities in sequencing, observational drawing etc...

54-57 Levelled worksheets based on Transport in Victorian Britain. This provides you with the ability to give differentiated work to different ability groups within the class whilst keeping to the same basic content and illustrations which are deliberately line drawings and colourable.

58-62 As above but on the theme of Florence Nightingale, a famous person from History who is also an appropriate person to study with KS1 children in a cross-phase class.